CONTENTS

JUNE 2017 • VOL. 231 • NO. 6 • OFFICIAL JOURNAL OF THE NATIONAL GEOG

D0480970

FRONT

VISIONS

EXPLORE
Progress: 3-D paintings, diverse comics, holograms

STARTALK
Neuroscientist and TV star Mayim Bialik on the status of women in STEM fields.

FEATURES

PHOTO: DOUG PERRINE, LAVA OCEAN TOURS

CONTENTS

ELSEWHERE

TELEVISION

IMAGINING WHAT LIFE WILL BE LIKE IN *YEAR MILLION*

If we're just in the infancy of technologies such as virtual reality and artificial intelligence, what will the future bring? Perhaps a metaverse (right), where one person's mind creates a simulated world that others also inhabit. It's one of the futuristic visions explored in the six-part global miniseries *Year Million,* airing Mondays at 9/8c starting May 15 on National Geographic.

TELEVISION

BREAKTHROUGH DELVES INTO DISCOVERIES

The series *Breakthrough* follows scientists whose work—on cancer cures, cybersecurity, drones, and more—could change the world. It also looks at the discoveries' social, ethical, and economic implications. Episodes air Tuesdays through June 6, at 10/9c on National Geographic.

NAT GEO WILD

MAN VS. OCTOPUS: WHO HAS THE EDGE?

The octopus, one of Earth's most intelligent invertebrates, can grow as large as a hundred pounds and have a 16-foot arm span. See how an octopus compares—in strategy, strength, and more—when pitted against a human. The face-off airs June 4 at 9/8c on Nat Geo WILD.

BOOKS

ANIMAL PARENTING TO WARM THE HEART

Two books full of inspiring stories and portraits of animal families are the perfect way to celebrate Mother's Day and Father's Day. *The Wisdom of Moms: Love and Lessons From the Animal Kingdom* and *Amazing Dads: Love and Lessons From the Animal Kingdom* are available wherever books are sold, and at *shopng.com/books.*

Subscriptions   For subscriptions or changes of address, contact Customer Service at *ngmservice.com* or call 1-800-647-5463. Outside the U.S. or Canada call +1-813-979-6845. We occasionally make our subscriber names available to companies whose products or services might be of interest to you. If you prefer not to be included, you may request that your name be removed from promotion lists by calling 1-800-NGS-LINE (647-5463). To opt out of future direct mail from other organizations, visit *DMAchoice.org,* or mail a request to: DMA Choice, c/o Data & Marketing Association, P.O. Box 643, Carmel, NY 10512.

NATIONAL GEOGRAPHIC (ISSN 0027-9358) PUBLISHED MONTHLY BY NATIONAL GEOGRAPHIC PARTNERS, LLC, 1145 17TH ST. NW, WASHINGTON, DC 20036. ONE YEAR MEMBERSHIP: $39.00 U.S. DELIVERY, $44.00 TO CANADA, $51.00 TO INTERNATIONAL ADDRESSES. SINGLE ISSUE: $7.00 U.S. DELIVERY, $10.00 CANADA, $15.00 INTERNATIONAL. (ALL PRICES IN U.S. FUNDS; INCLUDES SHIPPING AND HANDLING.) PERIODICALS POSTAGE PAID AT WASHINGTON, DC, AND ADDITIONAL MAILING OFFICES. POSTMASTER: SEND ADDRESS CHANGES TO NATIONAL GEOGRAPHIC, P.O. BOX 62130, TAMPA, FL 33662. IN CANADA, AGREEMENT NUMBER 40063649, RETURN UNDELIVERABLE ADDRESSES TO NATIONAL GEOGRAPHIC, P.O. BOX 4412, STN. A, TORONTO, ONTARIO M5W 3W2. UNITED KINGDOM NEWSSTAND PRICE £5.99. REPR. EN FRANCE: EMD FRANCE SA, BP 1029, 59011 LILLE CEDEX; TEL. 320.300.302; CPPAP 0715U89037; DIRECTEUR PUBLICATION: D. TASSINARI DIR. RESP. ITALY; RAPP IMD SRL, VIA G. DA VELATE 11, 20162 MILANO; AUT. TRIB. MI 258 26/5/84 POSTE ITALIANE SPA; SPED. ABB. POST. DL 353/2003 (CONV L.27/02/2004 N.46) ART 1 C. 1 DCB MILANO STAMPA QUAD/GRAPHICS, MARTINSBURG, WV 25401. MEMBERS: IF THE POSTAL SERVICE ALERTS US THAT YOUR MAGAZINE IS UNDELIVERABLE, WE HAVE NO FURTHER OBLIGATION UNLESS WE RECEIVE A CORRECTED ADDRESS WITHIN TWO YEARS.

Asian Small-clawed Otter *(Aonyx cinereus)*
Size: Head and body length, 36 - 44 cm; tail, 22.5 - 27 cm **Weight:** 2.4 - 3.8 kg **Habitat:** Wetland ecosystems with small pools of stagnant water **Surviving number:** Unknown; populations declining

ASIA

Indian Ocean

Photographed by Gerard Lacz

WILDLIFE AS CANON SEES IT

Social life. The opposite of a wallflower, the Asian small-clawed otter is always up for playtime, grooming and interactions of all kinds with its fellow group members. These otters communicate with seven structurally different vocalizations, forage together for crabs, shellfish, snakes, insects and more, and even help raise one another's young. But their cooperative, all-for-one and one-for-all lifestyle is under serious threat due to habitat destruction and degradation, as well as poaching for the fur and pet trades.

As Canon sees it, images have the power to raise awareness of the threats facing endangered species and the natural environment, helping us make the world a better place.

EOS System

Canon

FIND THE TRUTH AND PRINT IT

When I was a child in Ann Arbor, Michigan, my parents used to load my sister and me into the car and drive to my grandparents' house near Detroit.

My grandparents were immigrants from Russia and Poland. They spoke broken, heavily accented English with a lot of Yiddish sprinkled in.

My grandfather was a pugnacious, up-by-his-bootstraps businessman who didn't get past fifth grade. But what he lacked in education he made up for in certainty. He won every argument, big or small, by trotting out what he called the "Actual Facts," usually at top volume.

After each visit, on the drive home, my sister and I would snicker about my grandfather's Actual Facts—a ridiculous, redundant phrase. *We* knew that facts were facts. Period.

In a newsroom where I worked 35 years ago, our motto was similarly unambiguous: Find the truth and print it. That was correct then, and it is now. So it astounds me today that, in the United States and elsewhere, we're talking about Actual Facts—to say nothing of "alternative facts," "fake news," and "post-truth." Clearly, it's the ideal time to publish this month's cover, a scientific exploration of why we lie.

When my grandfather distorted the truth, it was annoying, but it didn't really matter—the stakes were low. But now, when elected leaders around the world do the same thing, it's frightening.

What's even scarier, in this digital era, is how errors of fact proliferate instantly, and that so many people embrace the alternate realities. The trust gap between the public and experts, after widening for decades, is now a chasm. And as "certified" experts decline in stature, "self-declared" experts ascend.

This is the bad news. But there's also good news—and you are a big part of it.

One of the great joys of working here is witnessing the affection and deep trust that readers feel for National Geographic and the content that we publish across platforms. I believe we keep that trust by producing journalism that is honest and fair, grounded in science and evidence, designed to educate and inform.

Confidence in the integrity of our work enables us to defend it, civilly, to those with other beliefs. That seems like a good place to start if we're ever going to agree, let alone act, on *actual* facts.

Susan Goldberg, *Editor in Chief*

In a University of Toronto study, children were put in situations where they had to choose between lying and telling the truth while researchers observed their brain activity using neuroimaging headgear.

PHOTO: DAN WINTERS

NATIONAL GEOGRAPHIC

WE BELIEVE IN THE POWER OF SCIENCE, EXPLORATION, AND STORYTELLING TO CHANGE THE WORLD.

VISIONS

Vietnam
Decoratively dyed bundles of incense dry in Quang Phu Cau, a commune in Hanoi. The aromatic material — burned to mark life events and connect with the spirit realm — has been a hallmark of Vietnamese culture for thousands of years.

PHOTO: TRAN TUAN VIET

| DAILY DOZEN

EDITOR'S PICK Each day online we feature
the 12 best photos submitted to our Your Shot
community. This is one of our favorites.

Albert Dros
Leusden, Netherlands

Dros loves to shoot in Asia, but he knew photographing from
one of the highest residential towers in Busan, South Korea,
wouldn't be easy. He negotiated with officials for months to
get permission. Then one night he was escorted to the roof
with his fish-eye lens and pointed the camera down.

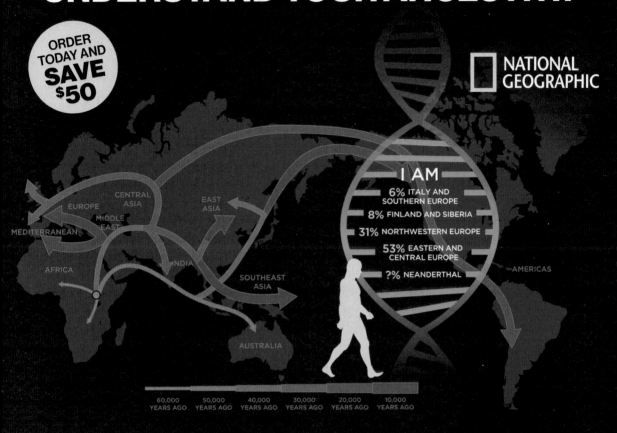

EXPLORE
PROGRESS

COLORING OUTSIDE THE LINES

By Jeremy Berlin

Bam! Thwak! Pow! Diverse superheroes are giving old stereotypes a beating.

As comic book and graphic novel sales in North America cracked one billion dollars in 2015, nontraditional characters—racial and cultural minorities, women, LGBT figures—are becoming major players. Some heroes in this inclusive pantheon are new. But well-known characters and brands are also getting a make-over: Marvel now has a black Spider-Man and a female Thor; Archie Comics' multiracial character Harper is disabled; DC's Wonder Woman recently officiated at a lesbian wedding.

Industry analyst Milton Griepp says once marginalized groups started appearing regularly in mainstream comics about 10 years ago. The rise of manga, with its heavily female readership, and the recent superhero films of Hollywood have been catalysts for the change,

he says. So have shifts in popular culture, laws, and demographics, and the ubiquity of the Internet.

It's not the first time superheroes have evolved. In fact, the latest changes are part of a continuum, says Ramzi Fawaz, author of *The New Mutants: Superheroes and the Radical Imagination of American Comics.* In the 1950s and '60s, writers and artists—mirroring and grappling with societal upheaval—began to feature outcasts and countercultural figures. In the following decades, identity politics and environmental issues joined the fray as well.

Today diverse characters have diverse creators. Steve Orlando, a bisexual writer, says his gay superheroes, Midnighter and Virgil, aren't just trailblazers; they're also "human and relatable."

"People tell me that Midnighter gave them the strength to be who they are," he says. "Some had waited their whole life for a character that looks like them. And that's what everyone deserves—a Peter Parker–style moment where you say, Hey, that guy's just like me. And that guy's a hero. Maybe I could be a hero too."

1. Prodigy
David Alleyne, a superhero with powers of mimicry, said he was bisexual in a 2013 issue of the *Young Avengers*.

2. Storm
The X-Men's "weather witch," Ororo Munroe, arrived in 1975 — the first black woman in mainstream comics.

3. Luke Cage
This black social justice hero got his super-strength in 1972, after a wrongful conviction and incarceration.

4. Black Panther
T'Challa, king of the nation Wakanda, is a physical, mental, and mystical marvel. He debuted in 1966.

5. Daredevil
Blinded as a child but armed with superhuman senses, Matt Murdock was created by Stan Lee in 1964.

6. Sunspot
In 1982 Roberto da Costa — a Brazilian able to harness solar power — joined the nascent New Mutants.

7. Dust
A mutant from Afghanistan who can literally turn into dust, this niqab-wearing character debuted in 2002.

8. Kyle & Northstar
Married to Kyle Jinadu, the superswift Jean-Paul Beaubier became, in 1992, the first openly gay superhero.

9. Dani Moonstar
A fierce Native American hero since 1982, she's part of an all-female team called the Fearless Defenders.

10. Karma
First appearing in 1980, this Vietnamese psychic is now one of the few openly lesbian superheroes.

11. Skin
The mutant Angelo Espinosa is a former Latino gang member who can alter his skin. He debuted in 1994.

12. Batwoman
Inspired by Batman, the tough Kate Kane was booted from the U.S. Army 10 years ago for being a lesbian.

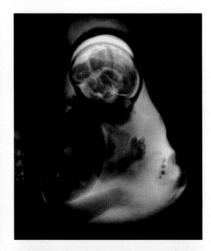

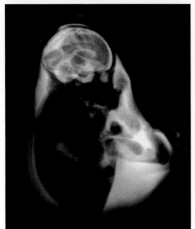

IMAGES: MORIAH E. THOMASON, WAYNE STATE UNIVERSITY SCHOOL OF MEDICINE (ALL)

BABY STEPS

By Catherine Zuckerman

MRI scans of human fetuses in utero – here, between 27 and 29 weeks of gestation – show the development of the brain and other organs and body parts.

Imagine if autism could be diagnosed before a baby is born. Rather than finding out around the child's third birthday, when developmental issues usually become noticeable, parents would get a head start on grasping the condition— and doctors would have an opportunity to strategize care in advance.

Diagnosis in utero is on the far horizon, says pediatric neuroscientist Moriah Thomason, whose research aims to solve some of the mysteries of the fetal brain. At Detroit's Wayne State University, she and her team use MRI technology to check the growth of a fetus's brain and map the neural connectivity within it,

creating a groundbreaking snapshot of how well the organ is functioning.

They focus on cases where there's danger of premature birth, Thomason says, because "we know that preterm children are at higher risk for developmental delays." Such delays are often blamed on stress or lack of oxygen during birth. Thomason's work suggests impairment may start in the womb, possibly with an undetected infection.

A clearer understanding will take time. The field moves rapidly, though, says Thomason. After all, it's only in the past few decades that prenatal ultrasounds have become routine.

THE SCIENCE OF PROGRESS

Water is pouring out of the sunny sky thanks to start-up Zero Mass Water, which invented a solar panel system to turn the air's moisture into potable drinking water. Panels can each produce five liters of water a day, and they've been installed in five thirsty countries.

An international team of scientists used mobile phone data to map poverty in Bangladesh. The type of phone, number of sent texts, and call minutes – all economic indicators – were combined with satellite imagery to produce a measure of the country's poverty.

Minuscule backpacks may transform dragonflies into tiny drones. Solar-powered devices developed for the DragonflEye project are strapped onto the insects and steer them by manipulating their nervous systems. Dragonflies can fly for thousands of miles and gather data out of reach of standard tools.

To boost vaccination rates, particularly in remote areas, scientists have been experimenting with administering vaccines more easily, from an inhalable dry powder for measles to a disk of dissolving microneedles for trial HIV vaccines.

FINGER PAINTING

By Natasha Daly

To appreciate a painting, we're taught to look for color, composition, and light. But how can a painting be savored by someone who's blind? Through touch, the one thing gallery placards tell you not to do. John Olson, a former photographer, and his team render paintings into fully textured 3-D models, like this version of Vincent van Gogh's "Portrait of Dr. Gachet."

The tactile paintings work as a way to reveal art to the blind because we don't see with just our eyes: We see with our brains. Research in the field of neuroplasticity—the brain's adaptability—shows that the visual cortex is stimulated by touch. Blind people perceive shapes with their existing senses, a process that broadly mimics that of sighted people, says Ella Striem-Amit, a Harvard neuroscientist.

Luc Gandarias, who's now 13, went blind suddenly at age seven. When he felt a 3-D rendering of Leonardo da Vinci's "Mona Lisa," he says he noticed her smile right away: "I could literally feel what you see when you look at it."

For Luc this means independence. "The feeling of being able to see it and form my opinion is like breaking down another wall as a blind person."

PHOTO: REBECCA HALE, NGM STAFF
PAINTING RENDERED BY 3DPHOTOWORKS

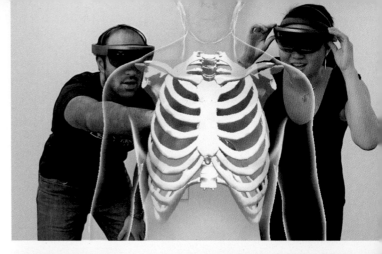

HOLO BONES

By Nina Strochlic

In 2014 radiology professor Mark Griswold was looking for a new way to teach anatomy. Running a cadaver lab can be expensive, and corpses offer surprisingly limited views into the body. In the midst of his search, he was invited to Microsoft's top secret testing facility. He expected to be shown a virtual reality headset, a potentially useful tool for teaching. Instead technicians outfitted him with something even more groundbreaking: a mixed reality headset, called HoloLens, the first self-contained computer that allows users to see holograms amid their surroundings.

When Griswold put on the headset, he was transported to a mountain on the surface of Mars. Standing beside him was a NASA scientist. They chatted and even made eye contact, but the scientist was a hologram—a real person beamed in from another room—and so was Mars, built out of rover images. The experience was so overwhelming that he had to sit down: "I immediately knew my world had changed that day." The headset, he realized, would be invaluable in the classroom.

Griswold and his colleagues at Case Western Reserve University and Cleveland Clinic set out to design a program for HoloLens that would revolutionize anatomy lessons. Last year they released HoloAnatomy, a demonstration application that transforms images into 3-D models of the human body's bones and organs and enables students to explore their shape and movement from every angle.

Virtual reality immerses users into an alternate world, removed from their surroundings. HoloLens is different: "Physical and holographic objects coexist and interact in real time," says Microsoft's Lorraine Bardeen. In classrooms this means students can communicate

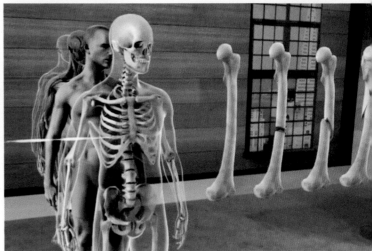

'I IMMEDIATELY KNEW MY WORLD HAD CHANGED THAT DAY.'

MARK GRISWOLD, CASE WESTERN RESERVE UNIVERSITY

with teachers, peers, and a holographic display during a lesson.

HoloLens has already been deployed to an array of fields, from aviation to fashion design. Elevator technicians use it to identify problems, and architects are creating holographic versions of blueprints to help conceptualize buildings. A medical technology company recently began using it to reinvent the operating room, so one day medical students who learned anatomy by hologram could perform surgery in a HoloLens-designed room.

In 2019 Case Western plans to open an anatomy lab designed with the help of HoloLens and using a curriculum built around the device. "I don't see a class on campus that won't be affected by the technology," says Griswold.

Case Western students test HoloLens, a holographic augmented reality headset. Below, an illustration of the display shows a body in 3-D.

ONLINE
To see a video of how the HoloLens allows students to examine bodies, visit *ngm.com/Jun2017.*

SAVING OCEAN SPECIES, FROM TOP TO BOTTOM

By Daniel Stone

The old proverb about not giving a man a fish but teaching him *how* to fish tends to apply literally to matters of ocean conservation. Rather than try to solve developing communities' problems for them—polluted coastlines, for instance, or depleted fisheries—many conservationists find that more lasting solutions come from giving people the tools they need to tackle the issues themselves.

Biologist Kerstin Forsberg is taking that approach to coastal and marine conservation, particularly regarding Peru's giant manta rays. "They are flagship species," she says, "and indicators of ocean health." Often incidentally caught by fishermen, they are listed as vulnerable by the International Union for Conservation of Nature.

Forsberg is a Rolex Awards for Enterprise laureate and a co-founder and director of Planeta Océano, a marine conservation nonprofit. In addition to protecting giant manta rays, her team conducts extensive studies on threatened marine environments, helps schoolteachers build networks to exchange information and compare lesson plans, and offers financial and technical help to fishermen and businesses that could fuel a growing ecotourism sector.

The approach appears to be working. Manta rays are now legally protected in Peru, and their image has gotten a boost too. Last year one of the country's magazines made a manta ray its cover model.

Conservation biologist Kerstin Forsberg is trying to protect manta rays by empowering the communities that interact with them.

ONLINE

FACEBOOK.COM /PLANETAOCEANO

ROLEXAWARDS.COM

National Geographic produced this article as part of a partnership with the Rolex Awards for Enterprise.

PHOTOS: JOOST VAN UFFELEN; FRANÇOIS SCHAER, ROLEX (FORSBERG)

From TV to Lab, and Back

Onetime child star **Mayim Bialik** earned a Ph.D. in neuroscience, then returned to acting on TV hit *The Big Bang Theory*—playing a scientist. It's given her a unique view of women's roles, in STEM fields and in general.

Neil deGrasse Tyson: So in your childhood, were there any science influences?

Mayim Bialik: There were a few. In junior high school I had a physics teacher who was very eccentric and would sometimes fall asleep while showing us slide shows, but he was a brilliant physicist. I went to a very unusual school: The 1980s sitcom *Head of the Class,* about a group of very smart and precocious children, was actually based on the school I went to. After junior high I had tutors on set because I was on this show *Blossom* from the time I was 14 to 19—

NT: No, you were not "on the show"— you *were* Blossom, to make that clear.

MB: Um, yes. OK. [Laughs]

In junior high I had no natural affinity for math and science—and all the boys in my classes worked so much faster than I did that I just assumed I must not be good at it. I didn't really understand the beauty of science and math and that whole world until later in high school, when this woman who was my biology tutor gave me the confidence that I could be a scientist. And after that, pursuing it in college, it was a party.

NT: This saddens me. That one single person made a life difference to you— but how many students are missing that one person?

MB: The first answer is: Many girls are. I'm sure we could run the statistics on it. And that's because of a historical difference in the representation of women in these STEM [science, technology, engineering, and math] fields and probably a cultural bias on the part of teachers and administrators. I think there's been a shift in education since I was in school in the '70s and '80s, but then it was like, Oh, you're not naturally good at math? Better try English—how's your Chaucer?

NT: There are people who presume that unless something comes easily to them, they should never pursue it as a career—without realizing that some of the greatest achievements you ever attain are because you busted ass to reach that point.

MORE THAN 3 MILLION KM² PROTECTED

BLANCPAIN HAS CONTRIBUTED TO DOUBLING
THE PROTECTED OCEAN SURFACE AREA

Fifty Fathoms Bathyscaphe

RAISE AWARENESS,
TRANSMIT OUR PASSION,
HELP PROTECT THE OCEAN

www.blancpain-ocean-commitment.com

JB
1735

BLANCPAIN
MANUFACTURE DE HAUTE HORLOGERIE

BLANCPAIN BOUTIQUES   ABU DHABI · BEIJING · CANNES · DUBAI · GENEVA · HONG KONG · LAS VEGAS · LONDON · MACAU
MADRID · MANAMA · MOSCOW · MUNICH · NEW YORK · PARIS · SEOUL · SHANGHAI · SINGAPORE · TAIPEI · TOKYO · ZURICH
www.blancpain.com

MB: Yeah. If I had not gone to college, I might have kept acting and been happy like that. But I loved going to UCLA and doing something that was very challenging academically. I loved doing research with adolescents with special needs—that was seven years of my life. It was exciting to get my Ph.D. in 2007. But in terms of time to raise my two sons, the flexible life of an actor was better than the long hours of a research professor.

NT: Fast-forward to 2010 and *The Big Bang Theory*. Who would have guessed how popular this show would become?
MB: Not me! I had never seen it before I auditioned.

NT: On the show you play Dr. Amy Farrah Fowler, who's a neuroscientist.
MB: She's actually a neurobiologist... but I get to say neuroscience things.

NT: How much of your professional self do you bring to your character?
MB: Since the job of an actor is to present a character even if you've never been in that profession, I guess I have the easiest job—I don't have to stretch that far.

NT: I try to imagine someone pitching the show idea to network executives: "Let's have six scientists, and they'll talk but you won't know what they're talking about, and they'll crack jokes and they'll laugh, but they won't explain it to you." I think it was low-hanging comedic fruit because no one had tackled it before.
MB: For sure. All the shows that I grew up with were about attractive people, and who had sex with who on which week. Meanwhile, our show is about the people who watch those shows.

NT: Might there ever be room in your show for a female character who's more sexualized—but also a full-on scientist?
MB: We did an episode where the Bernadette character, a microbiologist, poses for a "sexy scientist" photo shoot and Amy has a very big problem with it.

NT: I remember that episode. Your character, Amy, sabotages the photo shoot.
MB: That's right. When I do advocacy for STEM careers for young women, I'm

often asked, What do you think about [the sexy-scientist stereotype of] the white shirt open with the black bra underneath? And you know, I don't knock women or scientists who want to do that. For me, that's not the way that I choose to portray women in science. I don't think that's the only way to generate interest. It might be the only way to get a certain population of *men* interested in women in science... But it's not a personal goal of mine to further that notion of women scientists.

Part of my advocacy is to try to put a fresh face, a positive face, and a female face on these subjects. I think that a lot of women don't know the kinds of careers that are available to them. They may think what I did when I was in elementary school and junior high: I don't want to be alone in a lab for the rest of my life, in a nerdy lab coat and ugly glasses.

But then I got older and understood. Marine biology, working with animals, working in the environment—all those things are science. You like engineering? You want to do coding? Knock yourself out. There are many STEM careers that involve a lot of variety and a lot of creativity. And that's what I think we need to try and communicate to girls as young as possible.

NT: That was awesome! That's like the whole show right there.
MB: Thank you. And I didn't even have to take my clothes off to do it.

THIS INTERVIEW, DRAWN FROM A MARCH 2016 *STARTALK* TAPING, WAS EDITED FOR LENGTH AND CLARITY.

The cast of geeky-scientist characters in the sitcom *The Big Bang Theory* includes neurobiologist Amy Farrah Fowler (Mayim Bialik) and her boyfriend, physicist Sheldon Cooper (Jim Parsons).

Neil deGrasse Tyson hosts the television series *StarTalk* on National Geographic; see clips and full episodes at *natgeotv.com/StarTalk*. Find his book *StarTalk: Everything You Ever Need to Know About Space Travel, Sci-Fi, the Human Race, the Universe, and Beyond* wherever books are sold and at *shopng.com/startalk*.

IN SEARCH OF A RED-HOT LOVER

By Patricia Edmonds

Of these three hunky monkeys, which would you say has the most sex appeal?

That's easier to answer if you're a rhesus macaque *(Macaca mulatta)*—or Constance Dubuc, an evolutionary biologist at the University of Cambridge.

Since 2012 Dubuc and colleagues from New York University have studied more than 250 free-ranging rhesus macaques at a field site in the Caribbean. The goal: to learn how face color—which varies from pale pink to deep red in the species—affects reproductive success.

To isolate color's role in attraction, Dubuc showed each rhesus test subject two photos of faces in different shades of red. She found that dark red faces appeal strongly to females and somewhat to males—and she did so, in part, by tracking eye movements. "It's the same as with humans," she says. "If you see someone attractive in a bar or on the street, your eyes will linger a little longer."

Researchers also logged the monkeys' courtship acts by face color—and found that dark red–faced males got more propositions, from more females, than medium- or pale-colored males did.

In the best measure of reproductive success—number of offspring—dark red–faced females outdo paler ones. But for males, there's a twist: To get more couplings, and thus more offspring, they must have dominance in their group as well as a dark red face, Dubuc says. "Color alone wouldn't be enough."

RHESUS MACAQUE

HABITAT/RANGE/CONSERVATION STATUS
The nonhuman primates with the biggest geographic range, these monkeys are plentiful and live in varied habitats, chiefly in Asia.

OTHER FACTS
Many bird species sport colors that attract mates; rhesus macaques are one of the few mammal species that do.

PHOTOS: CONSTANCE DUBUC

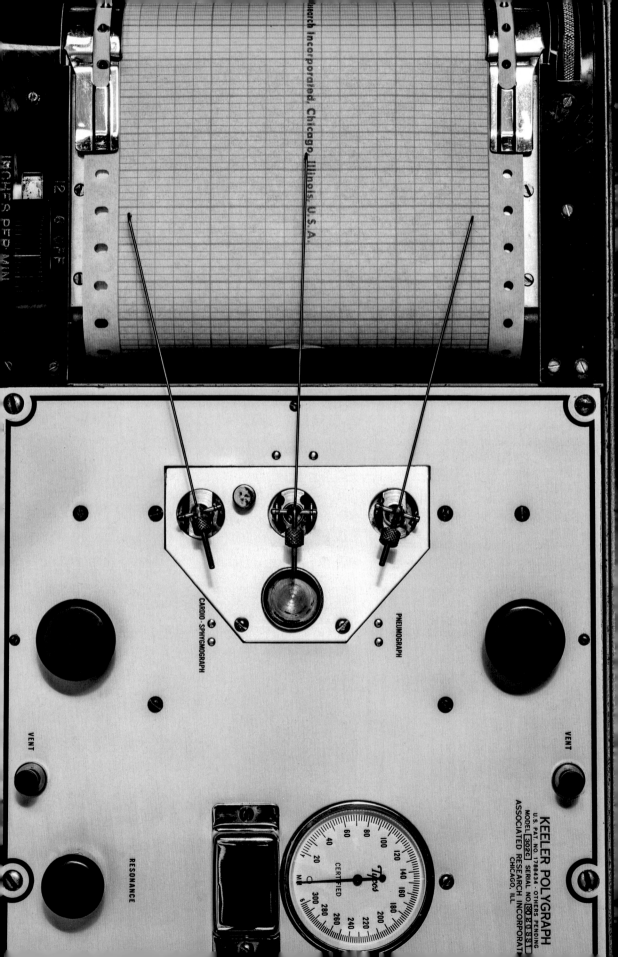

WHY WE LIE

Honesty may be the best policy, but deception and dishonesty are part of being human.

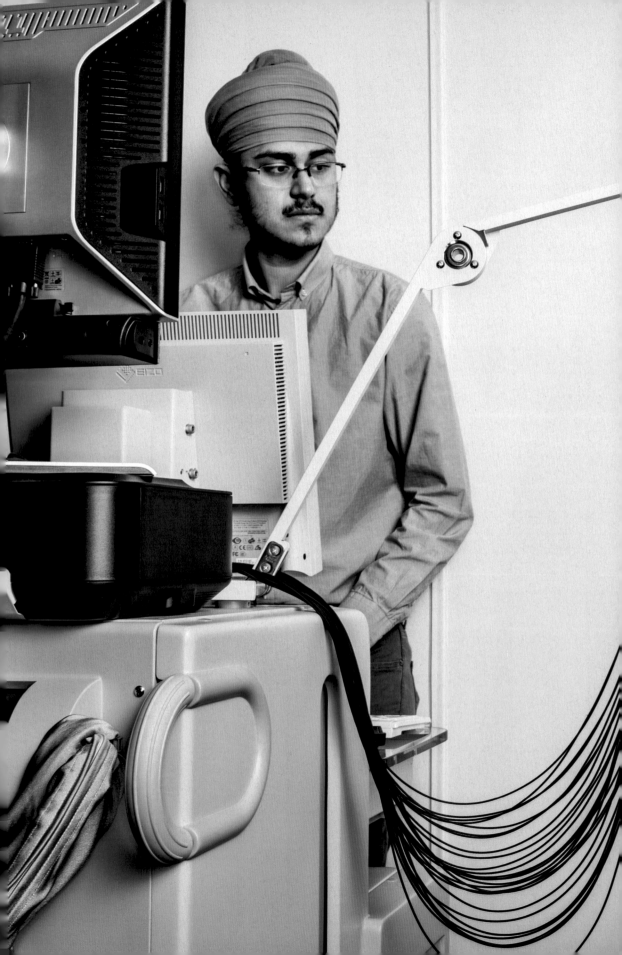

Learning to lie is a natural stage in child development. Kang Lee, a psychologist at the University of Toronto, has explored how children become more sophisticated liars as they age. Darshan Panesar, a research assistant, and nine-year-old Amelia Tong demonstrate functional near-infrared spectroscopy technology, which Lee uses in his studies.

THE ART FORGER
Lying for self-aggrandizement

Mark Landis, who says he was a failure as a commercial artist, spent nearly three decades imitating the works of famous painters, including this one in the style of folk artist William Matthew Prior. Posing as a philanthropist or Jesuit priest, he donated them to art museums and enjoyed being treated with respect. "I had never experienced this before, and I wanted it to go on," he says. "I have no feelings of conscience about this. When I was exposed and had to stop, I was very sorry."

BY **YUDHIJIT BHATTACHARJEE** // PHOTOGRAPHS BY **DAN WINTERS**

IN THE FALL OF 1989 PRINCETON UNIVERSITY WELCOMED INTO ITS FRESHMAN CLASS A YOUNG MAN NAMED ALEXI SANTANA, WHOSE LIFE STORY THE ADMISSIONS COMMITTEE HAD FOUND EXTRAORDINARILY COMPELLING.

He had barely received any formal schooling. He had spent his adolescence almost entirely on his own, living outdoors in Utah, where he'd herded cattle, raised sheep, and read philosophy. Running in the Mojave Desert, he had trained himself to be a distance runner.

Santana quickly became something of a star on campus. Academically too he did well, earning A's in nearly every course. His reserved manner and unusual background suffused him with an enigmatic appeal. When a suite mate asked Santana how his bed always seemed to be perfectly made, he answered that he slept on the floor. It seemed perfectly logical that someone who had spent much of his life sleeping outdoors would have no fondness for a bed.

Except that Santana's story was a lie. About 18 months after he enrolled, a woman recognized him as somebody she'd known as Jay Huntsman at Palo Alto High School in California six years earlier. But even that wasn't his real name. Princeton officials eventually learned that he was actually James Hogue, a 31-year-old who had served a prison sentence in Utah for possession of stolen tools and bike parts. He was taken away from Princeton in handcuffs.

In the years since, Hogue has been arrested several times on theft charges. In November, when he was arrested for stealing in Aspen, Colorado, he tried to pass himself off as someone else.

THE HISTORY OF HUMANKIND is strewn with crafty and seasoned liars like Hogue. Many are criminals who spin lies and weave deceptions to gain unjust rewards—as the financier Bernie Madoff did for years, duping investors out of billions of dollars until his Ponzi scheme collapsed. Some are politicians who lie to come to power or cling to it, as Richard Nixon famously did when he denied any role in the Watergate scandal.

Sometimes people lie to inflate their image—a motivation that might best explain President Donald Trump's demonstrably false assertion that his Inauguration crowd was bigger than President Barack Obama's first one. People lie to cover up bad behavior, as American swimmer Ryan Lochte did during the 2016 Summer Olympics by claiming to have been robbed at gunpoint at a gas station when, in fact, he and his teammates, drunk after a party, had been confronted by armed security guards after damaging property. Even academic science—a world largely inhabited by people devoted to the pursuit of truth—has been shown to contain a rogue's gallery of deceivers, such as physicist Jan Hendrik Schön, whose purported breakthroughs in molecular semiconductor research proved to be fraudulent.

These liars earned notoriety because of how egregious, brazen, or damaging their falsehoods were. But their deceit doesn't make them as much of an aberration as we might think. The

THE CHAMP

Lying for fun

Jacob Hall's desire to become a superhero inspired a tall tale that won him the West Virginia's Biggest Liar award and a golden shovel at last year's Vandalia Gathering, a folk festival in Charleston. "My stories would be pretty boring without deception," says Hall, who intends to spin yarns "for the rest of my life, if you can believe that."

WEST VIRGINIA'S

BIGGEST LIAR

2016

lies that impostors, swindlers, and boasting politicians tell merely sit at the apex of a pyramid of untruths that have characterized human behavior for eons.

Lying, it turns out, is something that most of us are very adept at. We lie with ease, in ways big and small, to strangers, co-workers, friends, and loved ones. Our capacity for dishonesty is as fundamental to us as our need to trust others, which ironically makes us terrible at detecting lies. Being deceitful is woven into our very fabric, so much so that it would be truthful to say that to lie is human.

The ubiquity of lying was first documented systematically by Bella DePaulo, a social psychologist at the University of California, Santa Barbara. Two decades ago DePaulo and her colleagues asked 147 adults to jot down for a week every instance they tried to mislead someone. The researchers found that the subjects lied on average one or two times a day. Most of these untruths were innocuous, intended to hide one's inadequacies or to protect the feelings of others. Some lies were excuses—one subject blamed the failure to take out the garbage on not knowing where it needed to go. Yet other lies—such as a claim of being a diplomat's son—were aimed at presenting a false image. While these were minor transgressions, a later study by DePaulo and other colleagues involving a similar sample indicated that most people have, at some point, told one or more "serious lies"—hiding an affair from a spouse, for example, or making false claims on a college application.

That human beings should universally possess a talent for deceiving one another shouldn't surprise us. Researchers speculate that lying as a behavior arose not long after the emergence of language. The ability to manipulate others without using physical force likely conferred an advantage in the competition for resources and mates, akin to the evolution of deceptive strategies in the animal kingdom, such as camouflage. "Lying is so easy compared to other ways of gaining power," notes Sissela Bok, an ethicist at Harvard University who's one of the most prominent thinkers on the subject. "It's much easier to lie in order to get somebody's money or wealth than to hit them over the head or rob a bank."

As lying has come to be recognized as a deeply ingrained human trait, social science researchers and neuroscientists have sought to illuminate the nature and roots of the behavior. How and when do we learn to lie? What are the psychological and neurobiological underpinnings of dishonesty? Where do most of us draw the line? Researchers are learning that we're prone to believe some lies even when they're unambiguously contradicted by clear evidence. These insights suggest that our proclivity for deceiving others, and our vulnerability to being deceived, are especially consequential in the age of social media. Our ability as a society to separate truth from lies is under unprecedented threat.

WHEN I WAS IN THIRD GRADE, one of my classmates brought a sheet of racing car stickers to school to show off. The stickers were dazzling. I wanted them so badly that I stayed back during gym class and transferred the sheet out of the classmate's backpack into mine. When the students returned, my heart was racing. Panicking that I would be found out, I thought up a preemptive lie. I told the teacher that two teenagers had shown up on a motorbike, entered the classroom, rifled through backpacks, and left with the stickers. As you might expect, this fib collapsed at the gentlest probing, and I reluctantly returned what I had pilfered.

My naive lying—I got better, trust me—was matched by my gullibility in sixth grade, when a friend told me that his family owned a flying capsule that could transport us anywhere in the world. Preparing to travel on this craft, I asked my parents if they could pack me a few meals for the journey. Even when my older brother snickered, I refused to disbelieve my friend's claim, and it was left to my friend's father to finally convince me that I'd been duped.

These lies that my friend and I told were nothing out of the ordinary for kids our age. Like learning to walk and talk, lying is something of a developmental milestone. While parents often find their children's lies troubling—for they signal

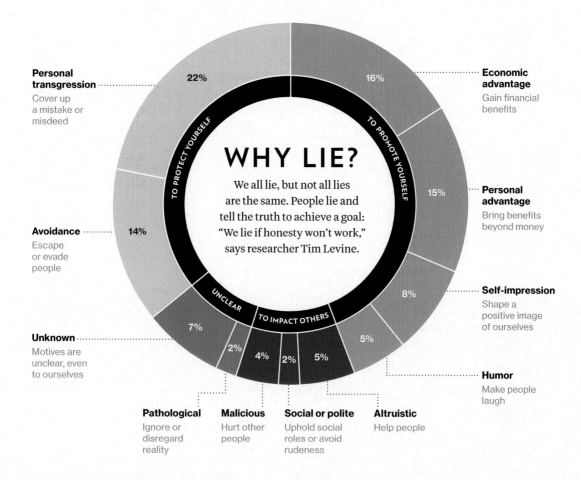

WHY LIE?

We all lie, but not all lies are the same. People lie and tell the truth to achieve a goal: "We lie if honesty won't work," says researcher Tim Levine.

TO PROTECT YOURSELF

Personal transgression — 22%
Cover up a mistake or misdeed

Avoidance — 14%
Escape or evade people

UNCLEAR

Unknown — 7%
Motives are unclear, even to ourselves

TO IMPACT OTHERS

Pathological — 2%
Ignore or disregard reality

Malicious — 4%
Hurt other people

Social or polite — 2%
Uphold social roles or avoid rudeness

Altruistic — 5%
Help people

TO PROMOTE YOURSELF

Economic advantage — 16%
Gain financial benefits

Personal advantage — 15%
Bring benefits beyond money

Self-impression — 8%
Shape a positive image of ourselves

Humor — 5%
Make people laugh

BENDING THE TRUTH

"The truth comes naturally," says psychologist Bruno Verschuere, "but lying takes effort and a sharp, flexible mind." Lying is a part of the developmental process, like walking and talking. Children learn to lie between ages two and five, and lie the most when they are testing their independence.

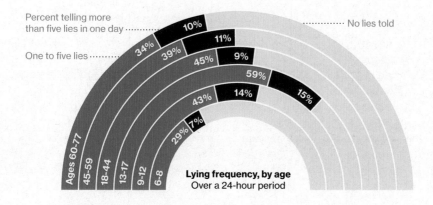

Percent telling more than five lies in one day

One to five lies

No lies told

Ages	Five+ lies	One to five	No lies
60-77	10%	34%	
45-59	11%	39%	
18-44	9%	45%	
13-17	59%		15%
9-12	14%	43%	
6-8	7%	29%	

Lying frequency, by age
Over a 24-hour period

RYAN MORRIS, NGM STAFF; SHELLEY SPERRY
SOURCES: TIMOTHY R. LEVINE AND OTHERS, *JOURNAL OF INTERCULTURAL COMMUNICATION RESEARCH*, 2016; EVELYNE DEBEY AND OTHERS, *ACTA PSYCHOLOGICA*, 2015; KIM SEROTA, OAKLAND UNIVERSITY

THE IMPERSONATOR

Lying for personal gain

Frank Abagnale, Jr., is now a highly regarded security consultant, but his brazen deceptions earlier in life inspired the 2002 movie *Catch Me if You Can*. Leonardo DiCaprio played Abagnale, who ran away from home at 16 and learned to survive by his wits, becoming a check forger, con man, and impostor. "I had to be creative in order to survive," he says. "I do and will continue to regret it for the rest of my life." Abagnale masqueraded as a pilot, a pediatrician, and an attorney with a Harvard law degree.

THE SECRET AGENT

Lying for country

Valerie Plame, a former CIA agent, worked undercover for two decades. In 2003 her cover was blown and her clandestine career ended when Bush Administration officials leaked her name to a newspaper columnist. She and her husband say it was done in retribution for his claim that the White House had exaggerated intelligence to justify the invasion of Iraq. What lesson did she take away from her years as a spy? "Most people," she says, "are more than willing to talk about themselves."

Watergate set the bar for presidential lies when Nixon insisted he played no role.

ON THE MORNING of June 17, 1972, five men were arrested after breaking into the Democratic National Committee headquarters in the Watergate building in Washington, D.C. The media, led by *Washington Post* reporters Bob Woodward and Carl Bernstein, doggedly pursued the story, exposing wiretaps, secret documents, and hush money. President Richard Nixon denied involvement in the scandal, declaring, "I am not a crook," in a nationally televised press conference. But the White House cover-up failed. Faced with almost certain impeachment, Nixon resigned from his second term in office on August 9, 1974.

OTHER FAMOUS FIBS

DONALD TRUMP: *"I won the popular vote if you deduct the millions of people who voted illegally."*

The president—who won the Electoral College but lost the popular vote—has kept fact-checkers busy with his steady tweets, many provably untrue. There's no evidence of significant voter fraud.

BILL CLINTON: *"I did not have sexual relations with that woman."*

Clinton's initial denial in early 1998 was subsequently proved false by the discovery of his DNA in a stain on intern Monica Lewinsky's dress.

ART BY TIM MCDONAGH; TEXT BY CLAUDIA KALB

the beginning of a loss of innocence—Kang Lee, a psychologist at the University of Toronto, sees the emergence of the behavior in toddlers as a reassuring sign that their cognitive growth is on track.

To study lying in children, Lee and his colleagues use a simple experiment. They ask kids to guess the identity of toys hidden from their view, based on an audio clue. For the first few toys, the clue is obvious—a bark for a dog, a meow for a cat—and the children answer easily. Then the sound played has nothing to do with the toy. "So you play Beethoven, but the toy's a car," Lee explains. The experimenter leaves the room on the pretext of taking a phone call—a lie for the sake of science—and asks the child not to peek at the toy. Returning, the experimenter asks the child for the answer, following up with the question: "Did you peek or not?"

Most children can't resist peeking, Lee and his researchers have found by monitoring hidden cameras. The percentage of the children who peek and then lie about it depends on their age. Among two-year-old transgressors, only 30 percent are untruthful. Among three-year-olds, 50 percent lie. And by eight, about 80 percent claim they didn't peek.

Kids also get better at lying as they get older. In guessing the toy that they secretly looked at, three- and four-year-olds typically blurt out the right answer, without realizing that this reveals their transgression and lying. At seven or eight, kids learn to mask their lying by deliberately giving a wrong answer or trying to make their answer seem like a reasoned guess.

Five- and six-year-old kids fall in between. In one study Lee used Barney the dinosaur as the toy. A five-year-old girl who denied having looked at the toy, which was hidden under a cloth, told Lee she wanted to feel it before guessing. "So she puts her hand underneath the cloth, closes her eyes, and says, 'Ah, I know it's Barney,'" Lee recounts. "I ask, 'Why?' She says, 'Because it feels purple.'"

What drives this increase in lying sophistication is the development of a child's ability to put himself or herself in someone else's shoes. Known as theory of mind, this is the facility we acquire for understanding the beliefs, intentions, and knowledge of others. Also fundamental to lying is the brain's executive function: the abilities required for planning, attention, and self-control. The two-year-olds who lied in Lee's experiments performed better on tests of theory of mind and executive function than those who didn't. Even at 16, kids who were proficient liars outperformed poor liars. On the other hand, kids on the autism spectrum—known to be delayed in developing a robust theory of mind—are not very good at lying.

ON A RECENT MORNING, I took an Uber to visit Dan Ariely, a psychologist at Duke University and one of the world's foremost experts on lying. The inside of the car, though neat, had a strong odor of sweaty socks, and the driver, though courteous, had trouble finding her way. When we finally got there, she asked me smilingly if I would give her a five-star rating. "Sure," I replied. Later, I gave her three stars. I assuaged my guilt by telling myself that it was better not to mislead thousands of Uber riders.

Ariely became fascinated with dishonesty about 15 years ago. Looking through a magazine on a long-distance flight, he came across a mental aptitude test. He answered the first question and flipped to the key in the back to see if he got it right. He found himself taking a quick glance at the answer to the next question. Continuing in this vein through the entire test, Ariely, not surprisingly, scored very well. "When I finished, I thought—I cheated myself," he says. "Presumably, I wanted to know how smart I am, but I also wanted to prove I'm this smart to myself." The experience led Ariely to develop a lifelong interest in the study of lying and other forms of dishonesty.

In experiments he and his colleagues have run on college campuses and elsewhere, volunteers are given a test with 20 simple math problems. They must solve as many as they can in five minutes and are paid based on how many they get right. They are told to drop the sheet into a shredder before reporting the number they solved correctly. But the sheets don't actually get shredded. A lot of volunteers lie, as it turns out. On average, volunteers report having solved six matrices, when it was really more like four. The results are similar across different cultures. Most of us lie, but only a little.

The question Ariely finds interesting is not why so many lie, but rather why they don't lie a lot more. Even when the amount of money offered for correct answers is raised significantly, the volunteers don't increase their level of

The White Sox shocked the nation when they threw the World Series.

NEARLY A CENTURY AGO, some members of the Chicago White Sox baseball team accepted a bribe—as much as $100,000 (about $1.4 million today)—to deliberately lose the 1919 World Series to the Cincinnati Reds. Suspicions arose in the first game after uncharacteristically sloppy pitching by the White Sox, who were heavily favored to win. "I don't know why I did it," pitcher Eddie Cicotte testified before a grand jury. "I must have been crazy." He and seven other players, including "Shoeless" Joe Jackson, were indicted on nine counts of conspiracy but acquitted by a jury. They were banned from the game for life.

OTHER FAMOUS FIBS

LANCE ARMSTRONG: *"I've said it for longer than seven years. I have never doped."*

As he had many times, the seven-time Tour de France winner lied to CNN's Larry King in 2005. Stripped of his titles, in 2013 he admitted to having cheated.

ROSIE RUIZ: *"I ran the race. I really did."*

Crowned the female winner of the 1980 Boston Marathon even though she barely broke a sweat, Ruiz denied cheating. Her title was revoked after evidence showed she hadn't run the full course.

THE CON ARTISTS
Lying to entertain

Apollo Robbins and Ava Do, who are married and business partners, use sleight of hand to entertain and educate. Robbins is an astonishingly agile pickpocket, perhaps best known for emptying the pockets of some Secret Service agents on a presidential detail. Do is a magician who has studied psychobiology. "We think of deception as the intent to distort someone's perception of reality," they say. "It is an impartial tool that can be used for good or bad, to inform or mislead."

THE CARD SHARK

Lying for strategic advantage

Raking in more than $32 million in tournament prizes, Daniel Negreanu has won more money than anyone in poker history. The Canadian-born superstar, who moved to Las Vegas 20 years ago, has traveled the world as an ambassador of the game and appeared on countless televised shows. "If you want to win at poker," he says, "deception is absolutely necessary." The trouble comes, he says, when players spend so much time deceiving competitors that "it infiltrates their personal life."

Many made claims to be the grand duchess of Russia, but all of them were frauds.

IT WAS A GRUESOME CRIME: In 1918 Bolshevik revolutionaries executed Russian tsar Nicholas II, the empress, and their five children. But did Anastasia, the youngest daughter, escape? Several impersonators exploited this hope, most famously Anna Anderson, an Anastasia look-alike who filed an unsuccessful suit in 1938 to try to prove her identity—and claim an inheritance. Anderson, who had supporters as well as detractors, died in 1984. A posthumous DNA test found she was unrelated to the Romanovs and appeared to confirm she was a Polish factory worker named Franziska Schanzkowska.

OTHER FAMOUS FIBS

JOAN LOWELL: *"Any damn fool can be accurate—and dull."*

Lowell famously fabricated her bestselling 1929 memoir, *The Cradle of the Deep,* about childhood adventures aboard a schooner with her sea captain father.

HAN VAN MEEGEREN: *"It was awfully hard work."*

The modestly talented 20th-century Dutch artist pocketed millions of dollars for his forged Vermeer paintings, which he baked in an oven to make the fresh paint look centuries old.

cheating. "Here we give people a chance to steal lots of money, and people cheat only a little bit. So something stops us—most of us—from not lying all the way," Ariely says. The reason, according to him, is that we want to see ourselves as honest, because we have, to some degree, internalized honesty as a value taught to us by society. Which is why, unless one is a sociopath, most of us place limits on how much we are willing to lie. How far most of us are willing to go—Ariely and others have shown—is determined by social norms arrived at through unspoken consensus, like the tacit acceptability of taking a few pencils home from the office supply cabinet.

PATRICK COUWENBERG'S STAFF and fellow judges in the Los Angeles County Superior Court believed he was an American hero. By his account, he had been awarded a Purple Heart in Vietnam. He'd participated in covert operations for the Central Intelligence Agency. The judge boasted of an impressive educational background as well—an undergraduate degree in physics and a master's degree in psychology. None of it was true. When confronted, Couwenberg's defense was to blame a condition called pseudologia fantastica, a tendency to tell stories containing facts interwoven with fantasy. The argument didn't save him from being removed from the bench in 2001.

There appears to be no agreement among psychiatrists about the relationship between mental health and lying, even though people with certain psychiatric disorders seem to exhibit specific lying behaviors. Sociopathic individuals—those diagnosed with antisocial personality disorder—tend to tell manipulative lies, while narcissists may tell falsehoods to boost their image.

But is there anything unique about the brains of individuals who lie more than others? In 2005 psychologist Yaling Yang and her colleagues compared the brain scans of three groups: 12 adults with a history of repeated lying, 16 who met the criteria for antisocial personality disorder but were not frequent liars, and 21 who were neither antisocial nor had a lying habit. The researchers found that the liars had at least 20 percent more neural fibers by volume in their prefrontal cortices, suggesting that habitual liars have greater connectivity within their brains. It's possible this predisposes them to lying because they can think up lies more readily than others, or it might be the result of repeated lying.

Psychologists Nobuhito Abe at Kyoto University and Joshua Greene at Harvard University scanned the brains of subjects using functional magnetic resonance imaging (fMRI) and found that those who acted dishonestly showed greater activation in the nucleus accumbens—a structure in the basal forebrain that plays a key role in reward processing. "The more excited your reward system gets at the possibility of getting money—even in a perfectly honest context—the more likely you are to cheat," explains Greene. In other words, greed may increase one's predisposition to lying.

One lie can lead to another and another, as evidenced by the smooth, remorseless lying of serial con men such as Hogue. An experiment by Tali Sharot, a neuroscientist at University College London, and colleagues showed how the brain becomes inured to the stress or emotional discomfort that happens when we lie, making it easier to tell the next fib. In the fMRI scans of the participants, the team focused on the amygdala, a region that is involved in processing emotions. The researchers found that the amygdala's response to lies got progressively weaker with each lie, even as the lies got bigger. "Perhaps engaging in small acts of deception can lead to bigger acts of deception," she says.

MUCH OF THE KNOWLEDGE we use to navigate the world comes from what others have told us. Without the implicit trust that we place in human communication, we would be paralyzed as individuals and cease to have social relationships. "We get so much from believing, and there's relatively little harm when we occasionally get duped," says Tim Levine, a psychologist at the University of Alabama at Birmingham, who calls this idea the truth default theory.

Being hardwired to be trusting makes us intrinsically gullible. "If you say to someone, 'I am a pilot,' they are not sitting there thinking: 'Maybe he's not a pilot. Why would he say he's a pilot?' They don't think that way," says Frank Abagnale, Jr., a security consultant whose cons as a young man, including forging checks and impersonating an airline pilot, inspired the 2002 movie *Catch Me if You Can*. "This is why scams work, because when the phone rings and the caller ID says it's the Internal Revenue Service, people automatically believe it is the IRS. They don't realize

THE PRANKSTER
Lying to tell stories

Some of the Internet's most viral videos and photographs have been staged by a secretive artist known as Zardulu, who rarely reveals the fabrications. "Like all myths," Zardulu says, "mine are established to engender a sense of wonder about the world, to counter our perceived mastery and understanding of it." Zardulu appears wearing a ram's head, symbolizing a journey into the unconscious mind, while the hierophant, an interpreter of mysteries, represents the shadow self.

THE FABULIST

Lying for professional gain

Jayson Blair is a life coach, seeking to help people define and achieve their goals. Before that, he was a fast-rising *New York Times* reporter whose career imploded in 2003 when he was discovered to have fabricated and plagiarized material in dozens of articles. "My world went from one in which I covered the deception of others to being the one doing the deception," he says, "and eventually, searching for answers to questions about why I lied and why others do so as well."

A gifted showman, P. T. Barnum exploited the public's desire to be amazed.

AT HIS FIRST SPECTACLE, in 1835, showman Phineas Taylor Barnum touted Joice Heth as George Washington's 161-year-old nursemaid. Crowds came gawking to see "the greatest natural & national curiosity in the world." Barnum profited from the public's hunger for entertainment by planting embellishments and lies in newspapers. His fabrication about Heth blew up after her death, when an autopsy found her to be no more than 80 years old. Barnum's flair for fake news culminated when, in ill health, he arranged for the publication of his own obituary so he could read it before he died.

OTHER FAMOUS FIBS

URBAN LEGEND: *"Paul is dead."*

Paul McCartney's rumored death in a 1966 car crash sent Beatles fans hunting for clues in the band's albums, including the 1969 release, *Abbey Road*.

ORSON WELLES: *"I can't imagine an invasion from Mars would find ready acceptance."*

On October 30, 1938, CBS Radio broadcast *The War of the Worlds,* a feigned account about aliens landing in New Jersey. Some listeners panicked, but Welles, who narrated it, expressed surprise that many had fallen for it.

that someone could manipulate the caller ID."

Robert Feldman, a psychologist at the University of Massachusetts, calls that the liar's advantage. "People are not expecting lies, people are not searching for lies," he says, "and a lot of the time, people want to hear what they are hearing." We put up little resistance to the deceptions that please us and comfort us—be it false praise or the promise of impossibly high investment returns. When we are fed falsehoods by people who have wealth, power, and status, they appear to be even easier to swallow, as evidenced by the media's credulous reporting of Lochte's robbery claim, which unraveled shortly thereafter.

Researchers have shown that we are especially prone to accepting lies that affirm our worldview. Memes that claim Obama was not born in the United States, deny climate change, accuse the U.S. government of masterminding the terrorist strikes of September 11, 2001, and spread other "alternative facts," as a Trump adviser called his Inauguration crowd claims, have thrived on the Internet and social media because of this vulnerability. Debunking them does not demolish their power, because people assess the evidence presented to them through a framework of preexisting beliefs and prejudices, says George Lakoff, a cognitive linguist at the University of California, Berkeley. "If a fact comes in that doesn't fit into your frame, you'll either not notice it, or ignore it, or ridicule it, or be puzzled by it—or attack it if it's threatening."

A recent study led by Briony Swire-Thompson, a doctoral candidate in cognitive psychology at the University of Western Australia, documents the ineffectiveness of evidence-based information in refuting incorrect beliefs. In 2015 Swire-Thompson and her colleagues presented about 2,000 adult Americans with one of two statements: "Vaccines cause autism" or "Donald Trump said that vaccines cause autism." (Trump has repeatedly suggested there's a link, despite the lack of scientific evidence for it.)

Not surprisingly, participants who were Trump supporters showed a decidedly stronger belief in the misinformation when it had Trump's name attached to it. Afterward the participants were given a short explanation—citing a large-scale study—for why the vaccine-autism link was false, and they were asked to reevaluate their belief in it. The participants—across the political spectrum—now accepted that the statements claiming the link were untrue, but testing them again a week later showed that their belief in the misinformation had bounced back to nearly the same level.

Other studies have shown that evidence undermining lies may in fact strengthen belief in them. "People are likely to think that familiar information is true. So any time you retract it, you run the risk of making it more familiar, which makes that retraction actually less effective, ironically, over the long term," says Swire-Thompson.

I experienced this phenomenon firsthand not long after I spoke to Swire-Thompson. When a friend sent me a link to an article ranking the 10 most corrupt political parties in the world, I promptly posted it to a WhatsApp group of about a hundred high school friends from India. The reason for my enthusiasm was that the fourth spot in the ranking was held by India's Congress Party, which in recent decades has been implicated in numerous corruption scandals. I chortled with glee because I'm not a fan of the party.

But shortly after sharing the article, I discovered that the ranking, which included parties from Russia, Pakistan, China, and Uganda, wasn't based on any metrics. It had been done by a site called BBC Newspoint, which sounded like a credible source. But I found out that it had no connection to the British Broadcasting Corporation. I posted an apology to the group, noting that the article was in all likelihood fake news.

That didn't stop others from reposting the article to the group several times over the next day. I realized that the correction I'd posted had not had any effect. Many of my friends—because they shared my antipathy toward the Congress Party—were convinced the ranking was true, and every time they shared it, they were unwittingly, or perhaps knowingly, nudging it toward legitimacy. Countering it with fact would be in vain.

What then might be the best way to impede the fleet-footed advance of untruths into our collective lives? The answer isn't clear. Technology has opened up a new frontier for deceit, adding a 21st-century twist to the age-old conflict between our lying and trusting selves. □

Yudhijit Bhattacharjee, a contributing writer, has also written about deception in his new book, *The Spy Who Couldn't Spell.* He wrote about baby brains in December 2015. **Dan Winters** is an award-winning photographer based in Austin, Texas. This is his first assignment.

Piltdown man, a clever fabrication of a human ancestor, created a sensation.

IN 1912 FOSSIL ENTHUSIAST Charles Dawson and his collaborator Arthur Smith Woodward, a geologist at the British Natural History Museum, announced the unearthing of humanlike skull fragments and an apelike jawbone from a gravel pit near Piltdown, England. Just a few years earlier, Dawson had written to Smith Woodward, saying he was "waiting for the big 'find.'" But Piltdown man, initially hailed as the missing link connecting ape to human, was a fraud: The bones were stained to resemble ancient fossils, and the teeth, from an orangutan, had been filed down to appear human.

OTHER FAMOUS FIBS

HWANG WOO-SUK: *"I created an illusion and made it look as if it were real. I was drunk in the bubble I created."*

The South Korean scientist claimed in 2004 that he had created a stem cell line from the world's first cloned human embryo. His data were fabricated.

MARMADUKE WETHERELL: *"We'll give them their monster."*

The British filmmaker had his stepson build a Loch Ness monster out of a toy submarine, using wood-plastic composite for the head, which appeared in an infamous faked 1934 photograph.

Life in the Balance

A warming planet threatens the Galápagos species that inspired Darwin's theory of natural selection.

Two marine iguanas seem unfazed by the presence of one of their mummified brethren, dead likely from starvation, on Isla Fernandina. Endemic to the Galápagos, these raccoon-size lizards forage for algae along the shore; larger males dive into the ocean. The algae they eat die in warm water, rendering Darwin's "imps of darkness" susceptible to climate change.

A scalloped hammerhead cruises past a school of steel pompano, endemic to islands in the eastern tropical Pacific. Fluctuations in water temperature increase the growth of barnacles on rocks and can also cause infections, visible as white patches on this shark.

After hunting, a Nazca booby returns to its nest near a thicket of prickly pear cacti on Isla Wolf. Scientists have been studying the birds elsewhere on the islands to gauge how long-term changes in their fish diet may hurt reproduction and depress populations.

By Christopher Solomon
Photographs by Thomas P. Peschak

J on Witman checks his air gauge, adjusts his flippers, and falls backward into the Pacific. Nearby, the ocean throws itself against Isla Beagle, one of a hundred-plus rocks, pinnacles, and islands that form the Galápagos archipelago, a province of Ecuador that straddles the Equator. Rebuffed, the sea retreats in a white flag of foam.

On a shelf above the spray, blue-footed boobies dance with the awkwardness of teens at a junior high prom. Below them on the rocks, an argument breaks out between two Galápagos sea lions. The scene could have looked and sounded the same when Charles Darwin sailed here almost two centuries ago. These creatures, fine-tuned to life on harsh isles, seemingly can weather anything, even time itself.

Suddenly Witman breaks the surface. "It's beginning," he tells me with a grimace.

He grabs his video camera from the dive boat and disappears underwater again. I plunge in after him. At 15 feet below the surface, Witman points me to a lobe coral, *Porites lobata*. It should resemble a mustard green pagoda, but instead it glows white against the seafloor's bubblegum pinks and AstroTurf greens. This coral is bleaching, a reaction to excessively warm water. Soon it will be dead.

At spots such as Isla Beagle, Witman and his crew are on the lookout for change. They've had no trouble finding it. They're taking the temperature of this seafloor community—literally and figuratively. During 2016's El Niño, the most intense climatic event here in two decades, the temperatures at his dive spots reached a peak of 88°F. (Overall, water temperatures in the Galápagos region were more than 4°F above their long-term average.) Witman, who has explored nearshore ecosystems from Easter Island to the Gulf of Maine for 40 years, fears that this bleached coral could augur an explosion of bleaching—as well as other dramatic changes throughout the environment here—in the years to come.

THE GALÁPAGOS ARE A STRETCH of 13 major islands that live as much in myth as on the map—a finch-crowded Brigadoon where Darwin arrived in 1835 and began to make observations that eventually would show him, and us, how life on Earth evolves. His *Origin of Species* would inform "almost every component in modern man's belief system," wrote evolutionary biologist Ernst Mayr.

As isolated as they may seem, the Galápagos aren't immune to the impacts of modern life: Climate change is coming to the cradle of evolutionary theory. Iconic species such as tortoises, finches, boobies, and marine iguanas could suffer. The famed ecosystems that taught the world about natural selection may teach us a lesson yet again, offering us insights into what's in store elsewhere. The Galápagos, says Witman, "are a fabulous laboratory for studying species' responses to climate change."

Before they were the Galápagos, they were Las Encantadas—"the enchanted ones"—warty islands laced with foam, flowing lava, and odd animals. "Man and wolf alike disown them," wrote Herman Melville. "The chief sound of life here is a hiss."

Whalers tossed those hissing tortoises into their ships' holds for food, filled water casks, and sailed on. They were right about the strangeness: Cut off from mainland South America by about 600 miles of water, nature here ran wild. Among

Silky sharks, the two pale forms here, are larger than humans. But they're dwarfed by a filter-feeding whale shark — the largest of fish — as they rub against it to scrape parasites off their skin. Isla Darwin is one of the few places where mature, often pregnant whale sharks make regular seasonal appearances.

the animals that made the voyage to the islands from the mainland, few survived. Those that did evolved into different forms by adapting to the conditions on each island. Those that could not adapt vanished into extinction.

But there are other changes happening here now—not just the evolutionary kind. Few places on Earth give scientists front-row seats to watch ecosystems shocked so drastically, sometimes repeatedly, in such a short time.

Now, as the globe warms, Witman, of Brown University, and other scientists are trying to understand what the future will look like here. Perhaps nowhere else on Earth is the cycle of life and death driven so dramatically by climatic events known as El Niños and La Niñas, when changes in temperature, rainfall, and ocean currents which can dissolve the carbonate skeletons of corals and mollusks, perhaps upending the ocean's food web.

Meanwhile, Witman and his team expect the bleaching of corals they're seeing around the islands to increase as a result of ultrawarm water caused by El Niños. A tropical ocean without these reefs is like a city without high-rises: With some of their homes gone, fish and other marine life that rely on corals have fewer shelters and places to eat. A rich ecosystem grows poorer, and then it won't weather shocks as well, including further shocks from climate change. Making matters worse, the islands are under pressure from a growing population—some 25,000 residents plus a crush of about 220,000 tourists a year.

So far the animals and plants of the Galápagos

Before they were the Galápagos, they were Las Encantadas, "the enchanted ones," warty islands laced with foam, flowing lava, and odd animals.

force striking fluctuations in weather and food availability, both on land and in the sea. And the influence of climate change is predicted to increase the rate of El Niños that come with intense rainfall from about once every 20 years to once every decade.

Models also project that the ocean near the Equator will warm slightly faster than the rest of the tropical Pacific, according to Andrew Wittenberg, a physical scientist with the National Oceanic and Atmospheric Administration. Sea levels are predicted to rise too: 22 to 30 inches by 2100 under some projections. Scientists also think that warming waters during the cool season could reduce the *garúa*, the dense fog that has blanketed the Galápagos' junglelike highlands for some 48,000 years. That could be catastrophic for life that depends on moisture from the fog. Also, as the world's oceans continue to absorb carbon dioxide produced by humans, the Galápagos are considered a hot spot for ocean acidification, have managed to survive this precarious balance. But the insults may be coming too fast and from too many angles to give them a chance to adapt.

ANCHORED IN A CURL of cove fit for a honeymoon brochure, Witman tugs a frayed wet suit over his striped surf trunks. Tan and fit from a lifetime of diving, Witman leads his crew of three divers back to the seafloor. One diver clutches a waterproof clipboard and peers among crevices like an overzealous census taker, counting pencil urchins. Witman's doctoral student, Robert Lamb, retrieves video cameras that had been left to document the behavior of passing residents such as Panamic sergeant majors and Mexican hogfish. Witman moves along the bottom, filming methodically. Playful sea lions lighten the scene by biting the divers' survey tape as if it were dental floss.

For the past 18 years Witman has visited the same dozen spots biannually to study how the

The Galápagos Bellwether

The islands that helped unlock the secrets of evolution may face intense El Niños more frequently as the climate changes. Increased temperatures and rainfall, plus potential sea-level rise, would create a host of stresses. Could species adapt, or would they disappear?

Isla Wolf

Isla Darwin
25 miles NW

NORTH AMERICA

MAP AREA

ECUADOR
SOUTH AMERICA

PACIFIC OCEAN

Isla Pinta
2,133 ft
650 m

Canal de Pinta

Isla Marchena
1,125 ft
343 m

Canal de Marchena

Isla Genovesa

Roca Redonda

Equatorial Undercurrent (source of upwelling)

PACIFIC OCEAN

EQUATOR

GALÁPAGOS ISLANDS
(ARCHIPIÉLAGO DE COLÓN)
ECUADOR

Volcán Wolf
5,600 ft
1,707 m

High-altitude dry area

Bahía Banks

Volcán Darwin
4,600 ft
1,402 m

Isla Santiago
(San Salvador)
2,974 ft
906 m

Volcán La Cumbre
4,843 ft
1,476 m

Volcán Alcedo
3,710 ft
1,131 m

Canal Isabela

I. Rábida

I. Beagle

Isla Seymour
Isla Baltra

Isla Fernandina

Bahía Elizabeth

I. Pinzón

Canal de San Salvador

2,835 ft
864 m

Isla Santa Cruz

Isla Isabela

Volcán Sierra Negra
3,688 ft
1,124 m

Cerro Azul
5,541 ft
1,689 m

Charles Darwin Research Station

Puerto Ayora

Isla Santa Fe

Canal de Santa Fe

Puerto Baquerizo Moreno

2,395 ft
730 m

Isla San Cristóbal

Puerto Villamil

Isla Tortuga

—600

Coral reef

0 mi   20
0 km   20
Bathymetry in feet

—3,000
—6,000
—9,000

2,100 ft
640 m
Puerto Velasco Ibarra

Isla Floreana

Isla Española
675 ft
206 m

Ecosystems		Normal conditions	Examples of changes during severe El Niño years	
	HUMID	Regular rainfall and dense fog sustain ferns, sedges, and cloud forests year-round.	Torrential rain rots roots and topples *Scalesia* trees that harbor some of Darwin's iconic finches.	Darwin's finches
	TRANSITION	Humid- and dry-zone species can coexist in the diverse forests found in this transitional ecosystem.	Tortoises are vulnerable to floods. Hotter weather can trigger upslope migrations from their dry-zone nests.	Giant tortoise
	DRY	With long periods of drought and little freshwater, endemic species have adapted to an arid climate.	Hot, wet conditions affect species like land iguanas that must regulate body and egg temperatures.	Galápagos land iguana
	UPWELLING	Nutrient-rich cold water from the Equatorial Undercurrent wells up from the deep, feeding ocean-dependent species.	Diminished upwelling of cold water sends sea lions farther for food. Abandoned pups usually die.	Galápagos sea lion

MATTHEW W. CHWASTYK, RYAN T. WILLIAMS, NGM STAFF. MANYUN ZOU
ART: MATTHEW TWOMBLY. SOURCES: CHARLES DARWIN FOUNDATION;
MANDY TRUEMAN, CHARLES DARWIN UNIVERSITY, AUSTRALIA

Small groups of endemic Galápagos sea lions on Isla Isabela's east coast hunt for yellowfin tuna, abundant here, by herding them into bays and then forcing them onto the rocks or dispatching them with a bite to the head. Sea lions are expected to decline as the climate changes.

Some of Darwin's finches lie arranged around an assortment of local seeds at the Charles Darwin Research Station on Isla Santa Cruz. Climatic extremes are the norm in the Galápagos. Birds that thrive here have beaks whose size, width, and shape have adapted to exploit the seeds available for them to eat.

communities that live on and around the seafloor—sponges, corals, barnacles, fish—interact. The Galápagos have some of the planet's healthiest tropical marine systems. The coral communities are thickets of biodiversity. "It's like a bush on land," Witman says, but instead of birds, the corals harbor symbiotic crabs and snails, as well as fish.

One reason the Galápagos are unique and so diverse—the reason, for instance, that penguins can share a beach with flamingos—is that four main ocean currents of varying temperatures bathe the islands. The deep, cold Equatorial Undercurrent, which travels about 8,000 miles across the Pacific, slams into the islands, upwells, and swirls around them, bringing to the surface nutrients that fertilize phytoplankton. This in turn fuels the rest of the marine food web. Everything is built upon this conveyor belt.

During El Niño the trade winds slacken. This weakens the upwelling of cold water and nutrients from the deep and also causes the pool of warm water in the western Pacific to expand toward the Galápagos. The conveyor belt nearly shuts down. The buffet closes. Marine life suffers dramatically. Some creatures may stop breeding; some even starve.

Some populations still haven't recovered from an extreme 1982-83 El Niño. The Galápagos damselfish is now believed to have gone extinct because of that event. Meanwhile, fortunes are often flipped on land, where El Niño usually brings drenching, life-giving rains to the desert isles.

La Niña overturns everything. Marine life prospers while terrestrial life languishes. Witman likens the natural, repeated cycle to a roller coaster: Deprivation. Recovery. Abundance. Repeat. During Witman's watch the Galápagos have experienced three major El Niños. In 2016 the warm waters led to reduced amounts of the algae the larger marine iguanas forage for in the sea.

Witman's question is this: If waters here are

PHOTOGRAPHIC FIELDWORK WAS FUNDED IN PART BY THE SAVE OUR SEAS FOUNDATION, THE PAUL M. ANGELL FAMILY FOUNDATION, AND FON (FOCUSED ON NATURE).

Finches on remote Isla Wolf have a tougher time procuring a meal than land birds elsewhere. To survive when already meager rations of seeds and insects can dry up completely, sharp-beaked ground finches become vampires; they peck at the base of booby flight feathers and drink the blood.

generally growing warmer, and if intense El Niños become more frequent, will the bad times hammer the seafloor communities so hard that they won't recover during the good times? And if so, will these communities turn into something else?

After the dive, to fortify his point, Witman shows me a snapshot of the coral on the seafloor below. "Normally this would be pink," he says. Instead it looks like a badly poured layer of concrete. The coralline algae, which form a crucial crust on which the rest of the community is built, have disappeared. Why? Witman suspects that the warmer seas of the recent El Niño goosed the metabolism of pencil urchins that graze on the algae, so they've mowed down the bedrock crust at many sites.

Meanwhile, black-striped salema and creolefish—once abundant plankton-eaters that provide food for sharks, sea lions, and other top predators—"have become uncommonly scarce during this strong El Niño," Lamb says.

The food web in the Galápagos already is being transformed by an array of factors to the point that some animals are having trouble adapting. The islands' population of blue-footed boobies has fallen by about half since 1997. Scientists think they know why: The Galápagos' sardines started to become rare (the reasons are not clear) in the diets of several predators around the same time. The boobies switched mostly to eating flying fish—which are harder to catch as they swim and are less nutritious. It's like going from all-you-can-eat steak to prison rations, says Dave Anderson, a Wake Forest University biology professor. Blue-foots often don't raise young when they're not eating well.

Could the loss of species diversity lead to a downward ecological spiral? "With fewer species," Witman says, "you have less resilience to threats."

ONE DAY IN MARCH 2016 ecologist Fredy Cabrera and I stride through a dim highland forest on

In a scene that could be 10,000 years old, giant tortoises rest in a mud pool in Volcán Alcedo's crater on Isla Isabela. For these reptiles, sand temperature during egg incubation determines sex. Predicted warmer air temperatures here could mean warmer sand and more females.

Isla Santa Cruz, the most populous island, home to about 15,000 people. Cabrera wears dirty blue jeans, a shy smile, and a T-shirt with a tortoise over his heart. We pass a boulder that issues a resigned hiss and retracts its head. We soon pass another boulder, then another. Giant tortoises seem to be everywhere.

Farther down, near the arid lowlands, Cabrera steps off the trail, removes a stiff wire grate from the ground, and begins to dig. Ten inches down he taps a buried cue ball. "There's a bad egg," Cabrera says in Spanish. Meticulously he excavates the nest. A wire barricade against predators wasn't enough to save these eggs. "Six out of eight are broken," Cabrera, an investigator with the Galápagos Tortoise Movement Ecology Programme, says. "Given those rains, that's not unusual." In January 2016, soon after the start of El Niño, damaging rains pounded the archipelago and inundated this patch of forest, causing many eggs to decay and crack.

Then there's the temperature question: For many reptiles, "if you are incubated at relatively cool temperatures, you're more likely to be a male, and if you are incubated at relatively high temperatures, you're more likely to be a female," says Stephen Blake, the program's coordinator. "If climate change leads to generally warmer sand, you may suddenly find that the sex ratio is skewed dramatically toward females." Scientists in several places around the globe, including the Great Barrier Reef and the Cabo Verde islands, are starting to see this phenomenon in sea turtles.

Failure to take pressure off the Galápagos' flora and fauna could kill the booby that laid the golden egg: Of the seven animal species that tourists rank most important to their visit—tortoises, sea turtles, marine and land iguanas, penguins, blue-footed boobies, and sea lions—all are expected to decline because of climate change, according to a 2011 vulnerability assessment by Conservation International and WWF.

ON ANOTHER HOT MORNING in the highlands, about 2,000 feet above the sea, Heinke Jäger follows a tourist group toward a grove of Scalesia trees. To the tourists nothing seems amiss.

Jäger, however, sees a world of wounds. Jäger is a restoration ecologist with the Charles Darwin Foundation, overseeing terrestrial invasive plant and animal species. Since the islands were discovered, in 1535, humans have brought many alien species—some intentionally, like goats, pigs, cats, and both ornamental and food plants, to name a few. Others, such as rodents, insects, and weedy plants, have been introduced accidentally. Some of these, like the blackberry, have become invasive.

Now the Galápagos, Jäger says, are home to more than 1,430 introduced species, including nearly 800 plants. Many don't cause problems, but some do. Invasive species are considered the greatest threat to the Galápagos and are one reason why UNESCO, in 2007, listed this place as a "world heritage in danger."

A friendly tour guide with a sober topic, Jäger points out Cinchona pubescens, or red quinine trees, one of the hundred most invasive species in the world. In the highest zone of Isla Santa Cruz, Cinchona shades and reduces native plants and, by changing plant-community structures, hurts endemic birds such as the Galápagos petrel, a seabird with the unusual habit of burrowing into the ground as much as six feet to nest.

Walking on, she notes brakes of invasive blackberries in the forest. Scalesia forests provide homes to entire communities of orchids, mosses, and birds. Just one percent of these forests, razed for agriculture four decades ago (they are now protected), remain on Santa Cruz. Where blackberry has invaded the remaining forest, it smothers the ground and prevents seedlings from rising and finches from nesting.

If the future here is indeed wetter, all vegetation may benefit, "but it's likely that the invasive species will really take off," Jäger says, in part because they are more flexible than the plants that are highly specialized to survive Galápagos life.

ACROSS THE ARCHIPELAGO a skiff nudges ashore on a remote black-sand beach on Isla Isabela, the Galápagos' largest island. Francesca Cunninghame steps over the rocking gunwale. In her hands she holds a cage draped in black cloth.

Her cargo: members of one of the world's rarest bird species. Cunninghame is taking them home.

The famed finches of the Galápagos, known as Darwin's finches—there are 18 recognized species (genetic studies are under way, and new species will likely be identified)—hold a prized, if erroneous, place in the popular imagination as the linchpin of Darwin's understanding of evolution. In truth Darwin didn't identify the islands where he collected finches and only realized his blunder upon returning home to Shrewsbury, England. So mockingbirds added to his later understanding of how one species might replace another through natural selection.

One of Darwin's finches is the mangrove finch, which today lives in just two isolated patches (totaling about 74 acres) of forest here. Invaders

aviary doors. Cunninghame opens the cages and gently removes 15 chicks one by one. Just four to eight weeks old and sooty in color, they seem less birds than puffs of cigar smoke.

Within minutes three chicks stand on the rim of their feeding dish, talking with their mouths full. For the next six weeks Cunninghame and others will remain here to release them gradually into the wild and conduct other research. Had they not collected and nurtured the season's first chicks and eggs, the birds all likely would have died, she says. For the past four years, researchers with the Charles Darwin Foundation—in partnership with the Galápagos National Park Directorate and in collaboration with San Diego Zoo Global and Durrell Wildlife Conservation Trust—have worked to boost the population.

Insults to the plants and animals of the Galápagos may be coming too fast and from too many angles to give them a chance to adapt.

already have found them—egg-eating rats and *Philornis,* a relative of the housefly that invades nests and has likely contributed to the local extinction of a warbler finch on Isla Floreana. *Philornis* larvae in nests increase in years of high rainfall according to one study, which could suggest more problems to come. Many land birds here are a bit like Goldilocks, preferring neither too little rain nor too much: Another recent study found that heavy rainfall led to decreased survival of fledglings. Today fewer than 20 breeding pairs of mangrove finches remain.

Carrying her precious load, Cunninghame walks barefoot across the burning sand and into a forest of tall mangroves. The light fades. The air cools. We walk deeper. A small wooden aviary appears. It's raised above the forest floor and contains three screened chambers joined together that keep out predators. Inside, Cunninghame and her three assistants set to work laying out breakfast for the birds. They shut the

Cunninghame still worries. "Any change, or increase in sea level, could potentially destroy this forest," she says. Mangrove finches prefer to nest in black and white mangroves that are buffered a bit from the open sea. It's unclear how well they would adapt if those forests vanished.

Cunninghame is more than three months pregnant and feeling a bit unwell, so she lies down on the floor of the aviary and watches the fledglings. She laughs when the birds bicker, and then smiles. Something heavy seems lifted from her. "They're back where they should be," she says.

There is a lot more work to do. For a few minutes, though, Cunninghame lies in the dappled light and listens to the little birds. For a moment it's the sound of victory. ☐

Christopher Solomon is a science writer based in Seattle and a contributing editor at *Outside* magazine. **Thomas P. Peschak** photographed the Seychelles for the March 2016 issue of *National Geographic.*

The Perils of Pale

*Models with albinism are popular in fashion, but around the world
people with the condition face scorn, health problems, and savage attacks.*

At a Hindu temple near their home in Delhi, India, three generations of a family with albinism pose for a rare family portrait. When two people with albinism — a recessive genetic trait — have children, the children will have albinism. Rose Turai Pullan (front row) and his wife, Mani (center), are joined by their six children, son-in-law (back row, second from left), and sole grandchild, Dharamraj Mariappan Devendra.

Students with albinism wear hats and sit in the shade for morning tea break at Lake View School near Mwanza, Tanzania, while their classmates head toward the sunny schoolyard. People with albinism have little to no melanin in their skin, making them more vulnerable to ultraviolet rays that can cause skin cancer.

By Susan Ager
Photographs by Stephanie Sinclair

Beneath a white, indifferent sky, a pale boy in a blue-and-red uniform shyly bows his head as tears begin to slip down his cheeks. He is retelling his terrible story.

Mwigulu Matonange was nine and Baraka Cosmas was five when assailants with machetes attacked them in their Tanzanian villages, taking body parts rumored to give power to witchcraft charms. They are fitted for free with prosthetics at Shriners Hospital in Philadelphia, arranged by Global Medical Relief Fund, a nonprofit that helps maimed children.

His father, visiting for the first time in two years, pulls out a white handkerchief. In the shade of a lone tree in the center of a Tanzanian schoolyard, the man reaches over to cradle his son's head and dab his eyes because the boy can no longer dry his own tears.

Emmanuel Festo, who is 15 years old, has spent much of his life learning to live with what he lost one night when he was six. Four men with machetes hacked off most of his left arm, most of the fingers on his right hand, part of his jaw, and four front teeth, intending to sell them. Emma, as he's known, is now a top student at a private boarding school. Although he stutters, he's healthy and strong, and he has friends. He's also an artist, drawing soccer players and Spider-Man and, for me, a detailed map of his country, by heart, using his cheek, chin, and shoulder to steer his markers.

Emma was born with albinism, a recessive trait he inherited from his dark-skinned parents.

His own skin is ivory white, his close-shaven hair pale orange, his eyesight weak. People like him have long been feared and scorned in sub-Saharan Africa, even by their families. Now they're being attacked. Some witch doctors claim their body parts, made into potions, powders, or charms, can bring wealth and success.

Detailed, gruesome records are kept by Under the Same Sun, a nonprofit organization working to end discrimination against those with albinism. Since the 1990s, in 27 African countries, at least 190 people have been killed and 300 attacked, most since 2008. The epicenter of this crime wave, which includes the robbing of graves, is Tanzania.

Almost a decade ago, when these attacks first drew widespread attention, Tanzanian officials rounded up many kids with albinism and, for their safety, sent them to rudimentary schools intended for blind and other disabled children. Many remain, living in squalid conditions. Until

2012 Emma shared a bunk bed with three boys at one of these government centers.

Emma tells me he loves his new school near Mwanza, where he has a bunk to himself. When I ask him about today's challenges, he says the kids mock his broken teeth. Then he makes a simple, heartbreaking confession: "Going to the toilet. My friend helps, but sometimes he doesn't give me toilet tissue, or just a small piece, and it's not enough for me."

Five hundred miles away in Dar es Salaam, Tanzania's biggest city, Mariamu Staford understands what Emma faces. She lost both arms at 25 but at 33 runs a small shop selling water and soft drinks. Her smile fills her round face, her toenails are painted red and blue, and she glows in a shiny green dress. Its sleeves hang limp at her sides.

Two of her attackers were released, and one died before trial. When I ask about the fourth—a neighbor—she closes her eyes and squinches her face as if she's about to let loose with a terrific punch line. "They set him free!" she shouts. "He's back in the village." Because of her weak eyesight, she adds, "the judge said I couldn't identify him. But we had lived near that guy for more than 10 years. I could identify him easily."

She is dependent on a young helper who makes change for customers, and a full-time caregiver who cooks and feeds her, dresses and undresses her, and washes her in a manner most people never want to need. Yet in other ways, she's independent, reading her Bible by using her tongue and chin to turn the pages. And she brags to me that she can text on her cell. I watch in amazement as she nudges the phone into place on a small table and then leans forward as if to kiss it. Instead she's typing with her teeth, which sounds like a hen pecking at the ground. *"Bwana Yesu asifiwe,"* she has written in Swahili. "Lord Jesus be praised."

Emma and Staford, like others with albinism, have little or no melanin, or pigment, in their skin, hair, and eyes. They are vulnerable to sun damage that can cause cancer. Emma's vision is so poor he must lower his nose an inch from my phone to see a photo of himself. Their challenges are similar to those of people born with albinism across the world—the sting of ridicule, poor vision, and sun sensitivity—but they also live in a region where a belief in spirits and spells is common, education is spotty, poverty is endemic, and albinism has been widely misunderstood. Men accuse their wives of sex with white men; parents believe their newborns are ghosts; nurses, as recently as a generation ago, told new mothers that venereal diseases must have bleached their children in the womb. In the past those with albinism were often killed at birth, or buried alive in tribal rituals.

Although the world's largest reported family of people with albinism lives in India—three generations, no exceptions—albinism is more widespread in Tanzania than in any other country. About one in 1,400 people there is born pale, and about one in 17 carries the recessive gene. Its occurrence varies greatly throughout the world. In Europe and North America the rate is only one in 20,000. On the San Blas Archipelago off the Caribbean coast of Panama, the rate among the Guna people is a staggering one in 70. There, locals say, dark and fair Panamanians live together without incident, the way tall and short people coexist.

Emma's secure schooling and Staford's caregiver are paid for by Under the Same Sun, founded by wealthy Canadian businessman Peter Ash. From his commercial real estate business based in Vancouver, he and his wife contribute about a million dollars each year to the nonprofit's $1.5 million budget. Ash is almost certainly the foremost advocate for people with albinism. He persuaded the United Nations to name June 13 as International Albinism Awareness Day and to appoint a UN expert, who traveled to Malawi and Mozambique last year as attacks there soared.

Almost all the nonprofit's money is spent from a fenced and guarded compound in Dar es Salaam. Under the Same Sun is paying to educate

The Mechanics of Melanin

Human skin, hair, and eye color is controlled by several genes that determine the amount and type of melanin pigment a person has. An inherited genetic mutation can interfere with this process, resulting in little to no melanin and raising the risk of severe sunburn, skin ulcers, and skin cancer. "OCA-2"— the most common type of albinism— is caused by a mutation that results in only small amounts of melanin.

INCIDENCE OF ALBINISM
Accounting for nearly half of albinism cases worldwide, OCA-2 is most widespread in sub-Saharan Africa. It's 14 times as prevalent in Tanzania as in North America and Europe. The Guna people of Panama have one of the highest rates.

Frequency of OCA-2 Albinism

GUNA PEOPLE (PANAMA)
1 in 70

TANZANIANS **1 in 1,400**

AFRICAN AMERICANS **1 in 10,000**

PEOPLE WORLDWIDE **1 in 40,000**

JASON TREAT, NGM STAFF; MEG ROOSEVELT
ART: BRYAN CHRISTIE
SOURCES: MURRAY BRILLIANT, UNIVERSITY OF WASHINGTON INSTITUTE FOR CLINICAL AND TRANSLATIONAL RESEARCH; RAYMOND BOISSY, UNIVERSITY OF CINCINNATI

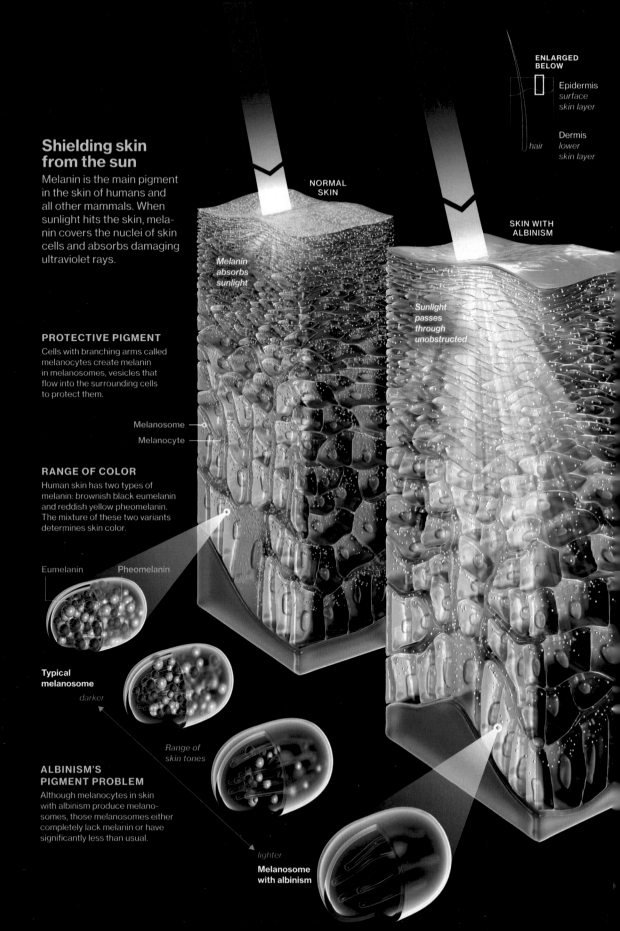

Shielding skin from the sun

Melanin is the main pigment in the skin of humans and all other mammals. When sunlight hits the skin, melanin covers the nuclei of skin cells and absorbs damaging ultraviolet rays.

PROTECTIVE PIGMENT

Cells with branching arms called melanocytes create melanin in melanosomes, vesicles that flow into the surrounding cells to protect them.

RANGE OF COLOR

Human skin has two types of melanin: brownish black eumelanin and reddish yellow pheomelanin. The mixture of these two variants determines skin color.

Eumelanin

Pheomelanin

Typical melanosome

darker

Range of skin tones

ALBINISM'S PIGMENT PROBLEM

Although melanocytes in skin with albinism produce melanosomes, those melanosomes either completely lack melanin or have significantly less than usual.

lighter

Melanosome with albinism

ENLARGED BELOW

Epidermis *surface skin layer*

Dermis *lower skin layer*

hair

NORMAL SKIN

SKIN WITH ALBINISM

Melanin absorbs sunlight

Sunlight passes through unobstructed

Melanosome

Melanocyte

At the Kabanga Protectorate Center in northwestern Tanzania, Yonge Kifunga, five, shades her sensitive eyes. Mbalu Keja, with two of her three children, lives at the center. To protect children with albinism after a wave of murders in 2008, the government sent many to facilities intended for blind and disabled students.

about 320 children to become professionals, seeking to change the stereotypes about—and the future for—people with albinism in sub-Saharan Africa, where for centuries they've been seen as curses and burdens: too poor-sighted to educate, too prone to sunburn while farming or fishing, and too strange to embrace.

As we're bumping over a road after meeting Emma, Ash tells me, "I view these kids as missiles, launched into society to blow up discrimination." Later he settles on the ground in the shade at another school, with 40 albino students from toddlers to teenagers. Big, beefy, and self-assured, he cheers as they shout out their career dreams—"Lawyer!" "Nurse!" "President!"—then pronounces them "ambassadors for change." Afterward, they swarm him. He lifts the chins of the bashful ones and says, "You must look at me. If you don't believe in yourself, the world will not believe in you."

UNDER THE SAME SUN'S STAFF of 26 Tanzanians, more than half with albinism, leads seminars on understanding albinism, usually in villages where people have been killed, attacked, or even kidnapped, never to be found. In those remote places, a variety of advisers, witch doctors, sorcerers, or diviners, called *waganga* in Swahili, are consulted for problems ranging from illness to a dry cow to an aloof wife. Prescriptions might include pulverized roots, herbal potions, or the blood of animals.

People desperate for success—in work or politics—sometimes seek more potent solutions. Some waganga insist that the magic they need thrives in their chalk-skinned neighbors. Albino hair and bones, genitals and thumbs, are said to possess distinct powers. Dried, ground, and put into a package or scattered on the sea, bits of people born white on a dark-skinned continent are alleged to make a fishing net bulge, or reveal gold in a bed of rock, or help politicians win votes.

On the stony southern shore of Lake Victoria in Mwanza, men and boys loiter in shorts, T-shirts, and flip-flops around their 40-foot, rough-hewn wooden sailboats. "What do you do to improve your luck?" I ask, and one fisherman explains in

Shamima Kassimu, eight, lives at the Kabanga center with three siblings who also have albinism. Some people with albinism, like Shamima, produce a little melanin. Exposure to the sun causes them to develop harmless dark blotches on their skin. The sun can also cause dangerous lesions that might turn into skin cancer if not treated early.

Swahili: "We can't just go into the lake without some kind of guidance or protection. Some of us believe in God, but the ones who believe in witch doctors get more than those who believe in God!" Everybody laughs and nods heartily. He continues, "We get from witch doctors something wrapped in cloth or paper." One man shows me with his fingers that it's shaped like a cigar. It can cost as much as 100,000 Tanzanian shillings—about $45—and is embedded in the boat. I ask what's in the packet. A tall, older man says simply, "We dare not look." I say, "I have heard that sometimes body parts of albino people are used for these charms," and before my translator finishes, all of them are frowning. One says, "Here nobody does that. They do it in the mines."

It's unclear exactly how such body parts earned their mystique, but academics trace their use as commodities to the turn of this century, when subsistence farmers saw more opportunity but

also more risk in fishing or mining for gold. Simeon Mesaki, a retired sociology professor from Dar es Salaam who studied witchcraft for decades, tells me that in Tanzania many go to church, but many more seek local wisdom. "God is far away, but the diviner is close by," he explains.

Most of the time a family member is implicated in the attacks. "Walking money" is a taunt thrown at people with albinism. The mother of a four-year-old boy who's in a safe school after men on motorbikes tried to snatch him from his front yard tells me, "I can't even trust my relatives, because if they want money, they'll do anything."

Ash offers me an analogy: "It's as if you had a dog in the backyard who was diseased, and your neighbor says, 'I'll give you one million dollars to bump off that dog.' That's how some parents view these children. A whole arm could fetch $5,000 at a witch doctor's, and let's say the father gets $500 or $1,000. It's a lot of money." In Tanzania the average annual income is about $3,000.

Since 2007 only 21 people have been convicted for murdering people with albinism in just six cases, according to Tanzanian prosecutor Beatrice Mpembo, who blames the low number on lack of cooperation from relatives. Ash says only about 5 percent of those arrested are convicted. No one has ever named any of the primary instigators of this violence—the affluent clients of the waganga.

ASH'S BOYHOOD FANTASIES never involved Africa. All he wanted to do was rocket into space. "You'll never be an astronaut," his mother told him, "but there are thousands of other jobs you can do." He served as a minister, then joined his older brother, who also has albinism, in business. Because he is legally blind, like most people with albinism, Ash employs a full-time driver, who chauffeurs him in a late-model, black BMW. His

At the Kabanga center, Melas Luge, 10, and sisters Zawia, 11, and Shamima Kassimu must hold objects close to see them. People with albinism have poor vision that is often little improved by glasses. They succeed in school by seeking front-row desks and counting on classmates to share notes.

$900 glasses are tinted against the sun, and the left side, for what he calls his "seeing eye," is fitted with a lens that magnifies six times.

By 2008, when he was 43, he had accumulated so much money that he was feeling ready to do something with the excess. A late night spent Googling "albinos Africa" left him horrified and sleepless. In those wee hours he read recent reports by Vicky Ntetema, a Tanzanian who was the BBC's bureau chief there.

Tipped off to attacks, including a teacher's murder of his 18-month-old son, Ntetema posed as a businesswoman to visit two traditional healers and 10 witch doctors, whose round thatched huts, topped with "antennae" made from sticks and cowrie shells, dot the rural landscape. "Two made it very clear, 'We kill,' and promised after I sent them a down payment they would give me body parts," she recalls. Each part, even hair, would cost her $2,000.

Her reports, to her surprise, angered Tanzanians. Witch doctors texted death threats to her. Countrymen questioned her patriotism. Government officials suggested this happened in other places, so why focus on Tanzania? For her safety, the BBC sent her into hiding outside Tanzania. Ash found her and, by phone, listened for hours.

He could not locate Tanzania on a map. He had never traveled farther than Europe. He had never carried his albinism as a purpose. But, he says, "I had an answer to the question of what would be next in my life." The next morning he checked flights to Africa.

Ntetema now leads Under the Same Sun's Tanzanian staff. She knows almost all of the sponsored children by name and can tell their stories.

Among the newest and sweetest is Baraka Cosmas, a tiny boy of six. His earnest face belies a tender spirit, even though his right hand was sliced off a year before. "I saw the blood flying all over the place," he told Ntetema after his attack, "and I called for my father, but he didn't come." When Ntetema told her team about his March 2015 attack, she ended her email: "God, this is too painful! When will it end?"

We first met in 2015, when Global Medical Relief Fund, a small nonprofit based on New York

At Lake View School, Rehema Hajji, nine, applies sunscreen to her younger sister, Fatuma, five, before they step into the sunlight. Sunscreen is expensive in sub-Saharan Africa, but nonprofit organizations distribute it for free. Many people with albinism in Tanzania die of skin cancer before turning 40.

City's Staten Island, arranged for Baraka, Emma, and three other maimed Tanzanian children with albinism to be outfitted with free prosthetics by the Shriners Hospital in Philadelphia.

Now in the lobby of a Dar es Salaam hotel, Baraka draws pictures in my notebook, holding a teddy bear I brought for him under his stub arm. Like Emma, Baraka has outgrown his prosthetic. He and one sister with albinism are going to school on Under the Same Sun's account. He and I resume our game of touching each other's face, saying, nose, *pua*; eye, *jicho*; cheek, *shavu*. He remembers how to count to 10 in English, using the fingers on his only hand twice.

He's seen his mother a few times, but frowning, he says, "My father is in jail." I don't ask why because I know: His father and a witch doctor are charged with assaulting him. Meanwhile he is happy, getting more hugs and kisses at his school, he says, than he ever did in his village.

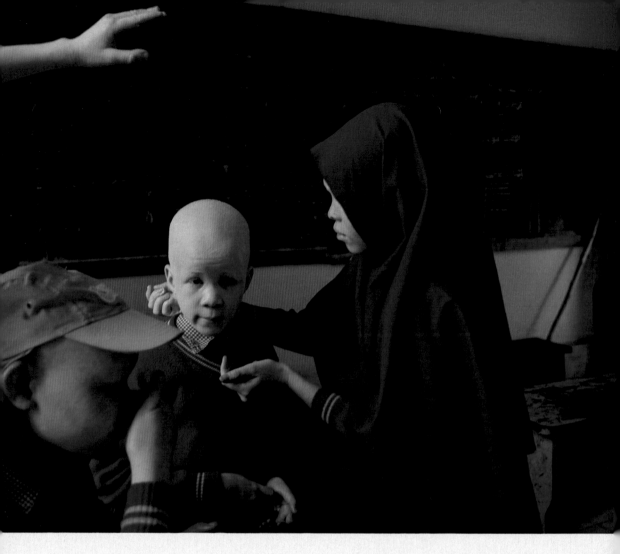

That evening Ash hosts a banquet for a dozen of the some 40 sponsored students who have graduated from college and found jobs with help from the organization's Godliver Gordian. She's a sparky young woman who cajoled employers, making the case for the students despite the fears she heard: "They're ghosts, white dogs, white monkeys. They're cursed. If you put them in your business, it could get cursed as well."

I meet a bank teller, a journalist, a lab tech, and a 23-year-old actor who starred in the 2013 indie film *White Shadow*, about a boy being hunted for his body parts. Hamisi Bazili told me his mother, who also had albinism, died of skin cancer after the film came out. She was 44.

FOR THOSE WITH ALBINISM in Africa, this is an all too common fate. Only recently have nonprofits begun to aggressively preach sun protection, distributing free sunscreen—which is otherwise rare and expensive, about $25 a tube—and wide-brimmed hats with flaps in back to cover the neck.

In Dar es Salaam I visit the Ocean Road Cancer Institute to meet Jeff Luande, considered the nation's expert on skin cancers that afflict people with albinism. As recently as 1990, he found that only 12 percent of people with albinism in the metro area lived to 40. The biggest killer: squamous cell carcinoma, easily treated if caught early.

He leads me to a ward where six men, two with albinism, lounge on their beds in street clothes. Saidi Iddi Magera gingerly unwraps the gauze around his head, revealing a raw, rough hole in his neck, below his left ear, big enough for a child's fist. Blood drips from it onto his crisp khaki pants. It's very advanced, Luande confides to me. Magera has languished in the bed for nine weeks, awaiting radiation from overbooked equipment.

Across the ward Msuya Musa lies hoping for a benefactor; he needs about $20 to get home, after

Recalina Hernandez, 28, and Eralina Hernandez, 26, sisters who live in Panama's San Blas Archipelago, belong to the native Guna population, which has an astounding one-in-70 incidence of albinism. Because the condition is common and is often seen as a blessing from God, they face little or no discrimination.

HOW TO HELP

To learn what you can do to help people with albinism, visit Under the Same Sun (*underthesamesun.com*) and the Global Medical Relief Fund (*gmrfchildren.org*).

yet another treatment. His cancer, three years old, consumed part of his left ear and turned the base of his neck a mottled red. "Now," he says, "I am trying to do fishing at night."

Neither man, each in his mid-40s, is likely to survive long, Luande says. They probably sought spurious help from waganga first, and medical help too late.

The children sponsored by Under the Same Sun know and demonstrate the sunscreen drill, smoothing it on the backs of their ears and in between their fingers. But the sun remains their daily curse. Without sunglasses, bright light stings their eyes, so they must close them for relief. Ash's group hands out sunglasses at every stop, and other groups test eyesight and distribute free spectacles, as they're called here, to help schoolchildren read blackboards.

In most of the world, people with albinism face childhood taunts and schoolroom frustrations, but they regularly find work and love and raise a family. Recently, in some careers, white skin and hair have even become an unexpected asset.

Consider musician Aaron Nordstrom, 35, vocalist for the alternative metal band Gemini Syndrome in Los Angeles.

"When I was in eighth grade, when I used to dye my hair strawberry blond, I looked like a pale Irish person. I even painted my eyebrows with a pencil," Nordstrom tells me, chuckling, but wiping away tears. "I spent most of my life trying to blend in. I was angry and depressed, on medications from the time I was 12 or 13." Eight weeks into high school, he tried to kill himself.

Playing piano and guitar with rock bands that were "angry without apology" gave him an outlet. He began to write his own music, including a song called "Basement" with the opening words: "Color-coded blasphemy, this really strange anatomy—is this really my life?"

Applause gave him confidence. Now his hair is in dreadlocks and his beard is hefty. "When we play on stage, everybody wears black except me. I wear white." He needs no makeup to distinguish himself: "It's God-given."

Kenya hosted the world's first beauty pageant for people with albinism just last year, to help lift

Enjoying a lively game of cricket outside his grandparents' house in Delhi, Dharamraj, six, along with his watchful aunt Pooja and uncle Ram Kishan, looks forward to days of greater acceptance and opportunity for people with albinism. Misunderstanding of the genetic condition has led to discrimination, ostracism, and even violence.

the stigma, while models with albinism are making a name for themselves on fashion runways around the world. Diandra Forrest, an African American from the Bronx, New York, was the first to be signed to a major agency. Confidence, she says, "was a work in progress, after so many years of being teased and misunderstood." At 28, she says she wouldn't trade her ethereal beauty: "I don't mind anymore being the albino model, because at least now people know what albinism is."

A few people with albinism also are making it to the top in Tanzania, including a couple of members of parliament and Abdallah Possi, who, in 2015, at age 36, was named a deputy minister— the first with albinism. Now an ambassador, he was also the country's first lawyer with albinism.

I MEET THE FUTURE of albinism in Tanzania when Acquilina Sami, 28, welcomes me to her apartment just outside Dar es Salaam, two cinder

block rooms with bars on the windows, a lace curtain over the door, and a crucifix on the wall. Tall and achingly lean, with wide hazel eyes and a high forehead, she begins her story: "My father left when I was one week old." He blamed her mother for her skin and her older brother's. "He didn't want to see us. He said, 'They are not human beings.'"

She feels lucky he didn't do worse. "In our culture, when a child is born with this, very soon they are thrown into the lake so they would not be seen. Yes," she nods. "It's known."

A Dutch woman who employed her mother paid for Sami's private schooling. She aimed to be an engineer until she realized that meant dealing with tiny numbers and symbols. Instead, with help from Under the Same Sun, she earned a degree in business administration. She now teaches at the Institute of Social Work, where she roams the classroom, engaging her students, lecturing without notes, rarely using the blackboard.

"Most come in wondering," she says. "I tell them a little bit about me; they get the ABC's of albinism." They grow to like her, she says. "Teaching is my dream job, my happiness: moving a person from one stage to another."

She believes the stigma against people like her is fading, although she interacts daily with strangers who stare at her, thinking thoughts she cannot read. Her life's challenge, she says, remains a simple but, in Tanzania, still a difficult one: "Peace of mind." ☐

Stephanie Sinclair, a frequent contributor, and her husband recently adopted two children with albinism from China. To read about their decision and their new life, go to *ngm.com/Jun2017.* This is the second feature **Susan Ager** has written for the magazine; her first was on Detroit, her hometown.

NICOLE CHAN

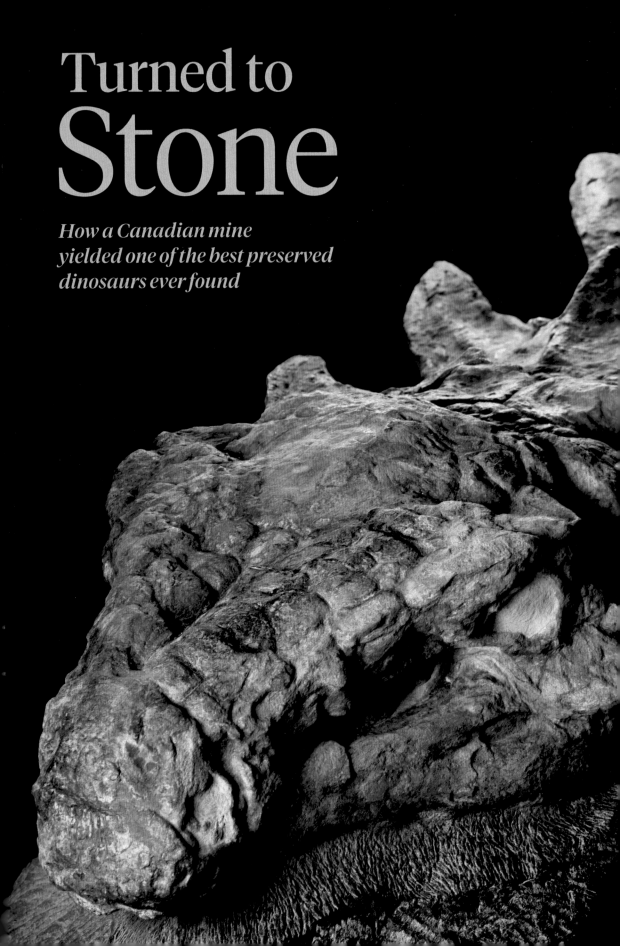

Turned to
Stone

*How a Canadian mine
yielded one of the best preserved
dinosaurs ever found*

Stunning Discovery

Some 110 million years ago, this armored plant-eater lumbered through what is now western Canada, until a flooded river swept it into open sea. The dinosaur's undersea burial preserved its armor in exquisite detail. Its skull still bears tile-like plates and a gray patina of fossilized skin.

93

Much like today's herbivorous lizards, the nodosaur's gut probably housed a modified large intestine in which it fermented its food.

The finely scaled pad of the nodosaur's forefoot (below) resembles the footpads of modern birds and big lizards.

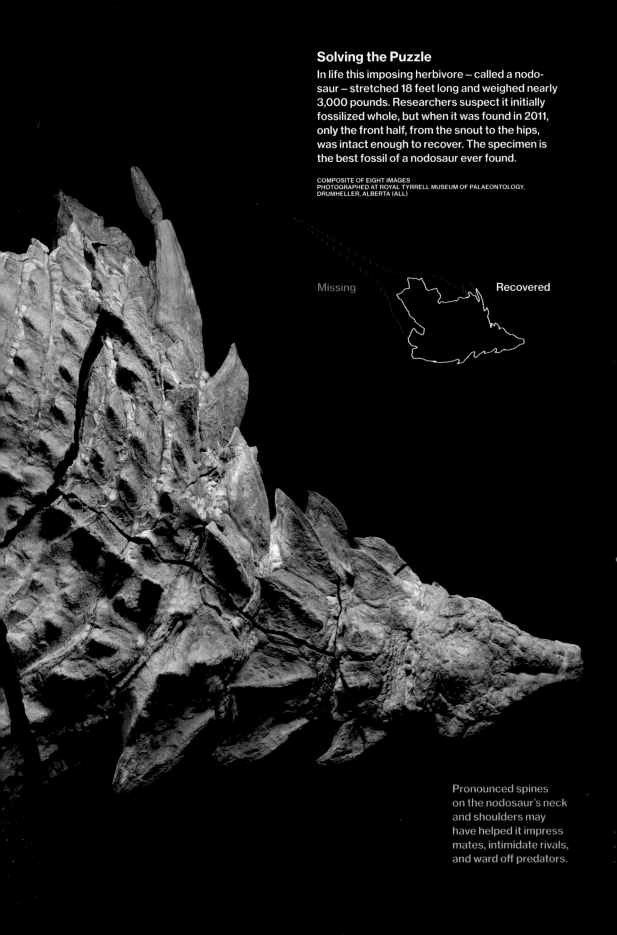

Solving the Puzzle

In life this imposing herbivore – called a nodo-saur – stretched 18 feet long and weighed nearly 3,000 pounds. Researchers suspect it initially fossilized whole, but when it was found in 2011, only the front half, from the snout to the hips, was intact enough to recover. The specimen is the best fossil of a nodosaur ever found.

COMPOSITE OF EIGHT IMAGES
PHOTOGRAPHED AT ROYAL TYRRELL MUSEUM OF PALAEONTOLOGY,
DRUMHELLER, ALBERTA (ALL)

Missing   Recovered

Pronounced spines
on the nodosaur's neck
and shoulders may
have helped it impress
mates, intimidate rivals,
and ward off predators.

By Michael Greshko
Photographs by Robert Clark

On the afternoon of March 21, 2011, a heavy-equipment operator named Shawn Funk was carving his way through the earth, unaware that he would soon meet a dragon.

That Monday had started like any other at the Millennium Mine, a vast pit some 17 miles north of Fort McMurray, Alberta, operated by energy company Suncor. Hour after hour Funk's towering excavator gobbled its way down to sands laced with bitumen—the transmogrified remains of marine plants and creatures that lived and died more than 110 million years ago. It was the only ancient life he regularly saw. In 12 years of digging he had stumbled across fossilized wood and the occasional petrified tree stump, but never the remains of an animal—and certainly no dinosaurs.

But around 1:30, Funk's bucket clipped something much harder than the surrounding rock. Oddly colored lumps tumbled out of the till, sliding down onto the bank below. Within minutes Funk and his supervisor, Mike Gratton, began puzzling over the walnut brown rocks. Were they strips of fossilized wood, or were they ribs? And then they turned over one of the lumps and revealed a bizarre pattern: row after row of sandy brown disks, each ringed in gunmetal gray stone.

"Right away, Mike was like, 'We gotta get this checked out,'" Funk said in a 2011 interview. "It was definitely nothing we had ever seen before."

Nearly six years later, I'm visiting the fossil prep lab at the Royal Tyrrell Museum in the windswept badlands of Alberta. The cavernous warehouse swells with the hum of ventilation and the buzz of technicians scraping rock from bone with needle-tipped tools resembling miniature jackhammers. But my focus rests on a 2,500-pound mass of stone in the corner.

At first glance the reassembled gray blocks look like a nine-foot-long sculpture of a dinosaur. A bony mosaic of armor coats its neck and back, and gray circles outline individual scales. Its neck gracefully curves to the left, as if reaching toward some tasty plant. But this is no lifelike sculpture. It's an actual dinosaur, petrified from the snout to the hips.

The more I look at it, the more mind-boggling it becomes. Fossilized remnants of skin still cover the bumpy armor plates dotting the animal's skull. Its right forefoot lies by its side, its five digits splayed upward. I can count the scales on its sole. Caleb Brown, a postdoctoral researcher at the museum, grins at my astonishment. "We don't just have a skeleton," he tells me later. "We have a dinosaur as it would have been."

For paleontologists the dinosaur's amazing level of fossilization—caused by its rapid undersea burial—is as rare as winning the lottery. Usually just the bones and teeth are preserved, and only rarely do minerals replace soft tissues before they rot away. There's also no guarantee that a fossil will keep its true-to-life shape. Feathered dinosaurs found in China, for example, were squished flat, and North America's "mummified" duck-billed dinosaurs, among the most complete ever found, look withered and sun dried.

Paleobiologist Jakob Vinther, an expert on animal coloration from the U.K.'s University of Bristol, has studied some of the world's best fossils for signs of the pigment melanin. But after four days of working on this one—delicately scraping off samples smaller than flecks of grated Parmesan—even he is astounded. The dinosaur is so well preserved that it "might have been walking around a couple of weeks ago," Vinther says. "I've never seen anything like this."

A poster for the movie *Night at the Museum* hangs on the wall behind Vinther. On it a dinosaur skeleton emerges from the shadows, magically brought back to life.

The remarkable fossil is a newfound species (and genus) of nodosaur, a type of ankylosaur often overshadowed by its cereal box–famous cousins in the subgroup Ankylosauridae. Unlike ankylosaurs, nodosaurs had no shin-splitting tail clubs, but they too wielded thorny armor to deter predators. As it lumbered across the landscape between 110 million and 112 million years ago, almost midway through the Cretaceous period, the 18-foot-long, nearly 3,000-pound behemoth was the rhinoceros of its day, a grumpy herbivore that largely kept to itself. And if something did come calling—perhaps the fearsome *Acrocanthosaurus*—the nodosaur had just the trick: two 20-inch-long spikes jutting out of its shoulders like a misplaced pair of bull's horns.

The western Canada that this dinosaur knew was a very different world from the brutally cold, windswept plains I encountered this past autumn. In the nodosaur's time, the area resembled today's South Florida, with warm, humid breezes wafting through conifer forests and fern-filled meadows. It's even possible that the nodosaur gazed out on an ocean. In the early Cretaceous, rising waters carved an inland seaway that blanketed much of what's now Alberta, its western shore lapping against eastern British Columbia, where the nodosaur may have lived. Today those ancient seabeds lie buried under forests and rolling fields of wheat.

One unlucky day this landlubbing animal ended up dead in a river, possibly swept in by a flood. The belly-up carcass wended its way downriver—kept afloat by gases that bacteria belched into its body cavity—and eventually washed out into the seaway, scientists surmise. Winds blew the carcass eastward, and after a week or so afloat, the bloated carcass burst. The body sank back-first onto the ocean floor, kicking up soupy mud that engulfed it. Minerals infiltrated the skin and armor and cradled its back, ensuring that the dead nodosaur would keep its true-to-life form as eons' worth of rock piled atop it.

The creature's immortality hinged on each link in this unlikely chain of events. If it had drifted another few hundred feet on that ancient sea, it would have fossilized beyond Suncor's property line, keeping it entombed. Instead Funk stumbled upon the oldest Albertan dinosaur ever found, frozen in stone as if it had gazed upon Medusa.

"That was a really exciting discovery," says Victoria Arbour, an armored-dinosaur paleontologist at Canada's Royal Ontario Museum. Arbour has seen the fossil at various stages of preparation, but she's not involved in its study. "It represents such a different environment from today and such a different time, and it has great preservation." (Arbour has begun studying a similarly well preserved ankylosaur found in Montana in 2014, much of which remains hidden within a 35,000-pound block of stone.)

The Canadian specimen literally defies words, in more ways than one. As this article went to press, museum staff were finalizing the creature's scientific description and hadn't yet settled on a common name for it. ("Mrs. Prickley," a reference to a Canadian sketch comedy character, didn't stick.) But already the fossil is providing new insights into the structure of nodosaurs' armor. Reconstructing armor usually requires educated guesswork, as the bony plates, called osteoderms, scatter early in the decaying process. Not only did the osteoderms on this nodosaur preserve in place, but so did traces of the scales in between.

What's more, sheaths once made of keratin—the same material that's in human fingernails—still coat many of the osteoderms, letting paleontologists see precisely how these sheaths exaggerated the armor's size and shape. "I've been calling this one the Rosetta stone for armor," says Donald Henderson, curator of dinosaurs at the Royal Tyrrell Museum.

Freeing this Rosetta stone from its rocky tomb, however, proved a herculean task.

After word of the discovery raced up the ladder at Suncor, the company quickly notified the Royal Tyrrell Museum. Henderson and Darren Tanke, one of the museum's veteran technicians, scrambled aboard a Suncor jet and flew to

3-D EXPERIENCE

Rotate, zoom, and examine every detail of this remarkable fossil using our 3-D model at *ngm.com/June2017.*

Shielded From Decay

Armored dinosaurs' trademark plates usually scattered early in decay, a fate that didn't befall this nodosaur. The remarkably preserved armor — seen here nearly life-size — will deepen scientists' understanding of what nodosaurs looked like and how they moved.

Blackish laceworks (below) trace individual scales, outlining the rows of flexible skin that alternated with the nodosaur's bony armor.

Deinonychus

Scientists speculate that a flooded river swept away the nodosaur, which floated out to sea uneaten and unscathed.

Trapped in Time

Few dinosaur fossils retain their true-to-life, three-dimensional shape, but the process illustrated here ensured that this nodosaur became a rare exception. Entombed in marine sediments, it lay in its grave for more than 110 million years, until an observant miner discovered it by chance.

From Burial to Discovery

The bloated carcass eventually ruptured and sank to the seafloor, where it was quickly buried by sediment.

1 Sediments enshrouded the nodosaur's body. Over time, minerals impregnated the dinosaur's tissue, preserving its 3-D form in a stony sarcophagus.

Seaway

Marine sediments

2 Layers of sediment accumulated and hardened into stone. During the ice ages, retreating glaciers deposited more debris. In time, vegetation stabilized the soil.

Dense forest and bog

Ice age sands and gravel

Cretaceous marine shale

Oil sand

3 Oil-sands miners dug through the nodosaur's back half before noticing it. A keen-eyed worker then spotted unusual patterns in the rock: the nodosaur's armor.

Pattern in stone spotted by the miner

5 in

Armor plate

Neural spine

Fossilized skin

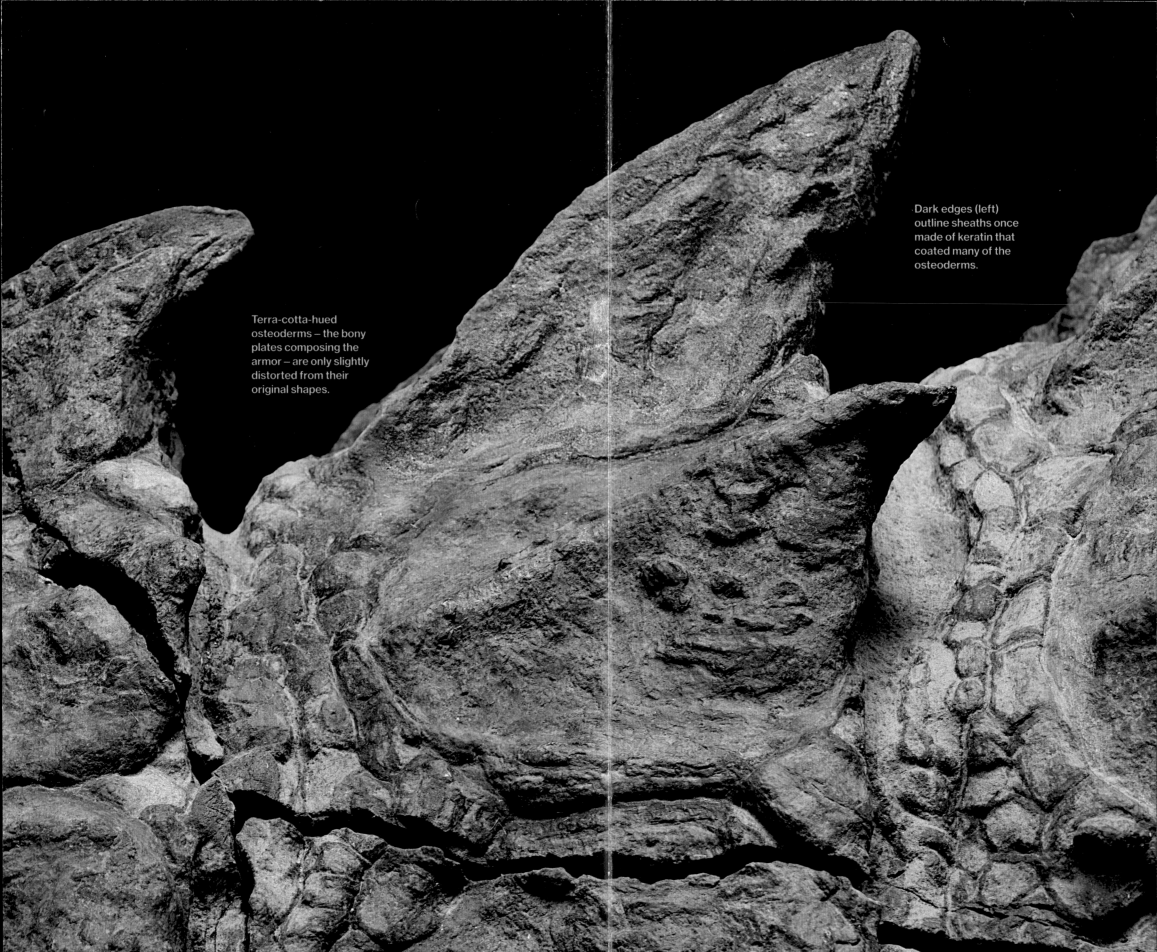

Terra-cotta-hued osteoderms — the bony plates composing the armor — are only slightly distorted from their original shapes.

Dark edges (left) outline sheaths once made of keratin that coated many of the osteoderms.

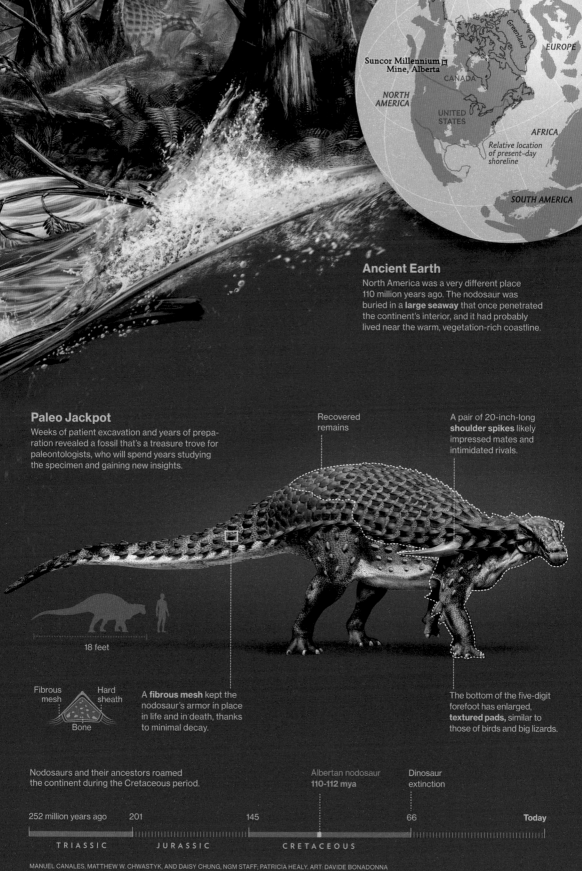

Ancient Earth

North America was a very different place 110 million years ago. The nodosaur was buried in a **large seaway** that once penetrated the continent's interior, and it had probably lived near the warm, vegetation-rich coastline.

Suncor Millennium Mine, Alberta

GREENLAND
EUROPE
NORTH AMERICA
CANADA
UNITED STATES
AFRICA
SOUTH AMERICA

Relative location of present-day shoreline

Paleo Jackpot

Weeks of patient excavation and years of preparation revealed a fossil that's a treasure trove for paleontologists, who will spend years studying the specimen and gaining new insights.

Recovered remains

A pair of 20-inch-long **shoulder spikes** likely impressed mates and intimidated rivals.

18 feet

Fibrous mesh
Hard sheath
Bone

A **fibrous mesh** kept the nodosaur's armor in place in life and in death, thanks to minimal decay.

The bottom of the five-digit forefoot has enlarged, **textured pads,** similar to those of birds and big lizards.

Nodosaurs and their ancestors roamed the continent during the Cretaceous period.

Albertan nodosaur
110-112 mya

Dinosaur extinction

252 million years ago | 201 | 145 | 66 | **Today**

TRIASSIC | JURASSIC | CRETACEOUS

MANUEL CANALES, MATTHEW W. CHWASTYK, AND DAISY CHUNG, NGM STAFF; PATRICIA HEALY. ART: DAVIDE BONADONNA
SOURCES: CALEB MARSHALL BROWN AND DONALD HENDERSON, ROYAL TYRRELL MUSEUM OF PALAEONTOLOGY; JAKOB VINTHER; C. R. SCOTESE, PALEOMAP PROJECT

Fort McMurray. Suncor excavators and museum staff chipped away at the rock in 12-hour shifts, shrouded in dust and diesel fumes.

They eventually whittled it down to a 15,000-pound rock containing the dinosaur, ready to be hoisted out of the pit. But with cameras rolling, disaster struck: As it was lifted, the rock shattered, cleaving the dinosaur into several chunks. The fossil's partially mineralized, cakelike interior simply couldn't support its own weight.

Tanke spent the night devising a plan to save the fossil. The next morning Suncor personnel wrapped the fragments in plaster of paris, while Tanke and Henderson scrounged for anything to

stabilize the fossil on the long drive to the museum. In lieu of timbers, the crew used plaster-soaked burlap rolled up like logs.

The MacGyver-like plan worked. Some 420 miles later the team reached the Royal Tyrrell Museum's prep lab, where the blocks were entrusted to fossil preparator Mark Mitchell. His work on the nodosaur has required a sculptor's touch: For more than 7,000 hours over the past five years, Mitchell has slowly exposed the fossil's skin and bone. The painstaking process is like freeing compressed talcum powder from concrete. "You almost have to fight for every millimeter," he says.

Mitchell's fight is nearly over, but it will take years, if not decades, to fully understand the fossil he uncovers. Its skeleton, for example,

Society Grants Your National Geographic Society membership helped support this project.

Last Meal?

Royal Tyrrell Museum technician Mark Mitchell slowly frees the nodosaur's foot and scaly footpad from the surrounding rock. Mitchell's careful work will preserve for years to come the animal's enigmatic features – including a cluster of pebble-like masses (left) whose location suggests that they may be remnants of its final meal.

remains mostly obscured in skin and armor. In some ways it's almost too well preserved; reaching the dinosaur's bones would require destroying its outer layers. CT scans funded by the National Geographic Society have revealed little, as the rock remains stubbornly opaque.

For Vinther the nodosaur fossil's most revolutionary features may lie at its smallest scale: microscopic remnants of its original coloration. If he successfully reconstructs its distribution, he could help reveal how the dinosaur navigated its environment and used its pronounced armor.

"This armor was clearly providing protection, but those elaborated horns on the front of its body would have been almost like a billboard," he says. This advertisement could have helped woo mates or intimidate rivals—and may have stood

out against a backdrop of rouge. Chemical tests of the dinosaur's skin have hinted at the presence of reddish pigments, contrasting with the horns' markedly light coloration.

In May the Royal Tyrrell Museum unveils the nodosaur as the centerpiece of a new exhibit of fossils recovered from Alberta's industrial sites. Now the public is marveling at what has wowed scientists for the past six years: an ambassador from Canada's distant past, found in a moonscape by a man with an excavator. ☐

Science writer **Michael Greshko** covers space, natural history, and other topics for National Geographic's website. Photographer **Robert Clark** has shot more than 40 stories for the magazine. His most recent book is *Evolution: A Visual Record*.

A State of Grief

Crime-scene investigators in Manila recover a body and gather evidence at an apparent drug-related execution. The victim, Angelito Luciano, 41, was a community volunteer who helped police with antidrug efforts.

As the Philippines wages a violent war on drugs, death rituals have become a cathartic part of daily life.

BY **AURORA ALMENDRAL**
PHOTOGRAPHS BY **ADAM DEAN**

As soon as Rick Medina saw the body slumped over the curb on the evening news last November, he knew it was his 23-year-old son, Ericardo. The victim—dumped on a quiet avenue in Manila, the Philippine capital—could have been anyone. His back was to the TV cameras, but a father knows.

The next morning his daughter Jhoy, 26, visited the morgue. Eight bodies were lined up on the floor. They had all died the same way: Their heads had been bound in packing tape, their chests and necks stabbed repeatedly with an ice pick. A cardboard sign left on Ericardo's body labeled him a drug dealer. According to his father, Ericardo never touched drugs; Jhoy says he dabbled in them. Either way, his killers meted out a final punishment without due process.

The plight of the Medina family has been repeated thousands of times in recent months in the Philippines, where Rodrigo Duterte rode a tide of populist frustration to a presidential

meant to console the family and deepen community ties. But they also have come to serve another purpose: substituting for justice at a time when many see the killings as committed with staggering impunity. Death rituals here outnumber ceremonies for either births or marriages, says anthropologist Nestor Castro of the University of the Philippines Diliman.

During the seven-to-10-day wake, the body of the deceased is never left alone. Chicks are placed on the coffin with food to peck at—to symbolically prick the conscience of the killer. A pot is broken to break the cycle of death—to prevent more deaths from following. Personal items are tucked into the casket for the afterlife. When a casket leaves the home, it is spun three times, and coins are thrown along the path of the funeral procession to pay for travels to the afterlife.

The family members may also await a *paramdam,* a visit from the spirit of the deceased. The appearance serves as a final message—a chance for solace. The paramdam takes on particular urgency when the death was sudden or mysterious.

The night before his funeral, Ericardo's sister said, he visited her in a dream. "He was smiling," she said. It gave Jhoy comfort to know that Ericardo was not angry, that his spirit wasn't lingering in this world, demanding vengeance. "It was just like him," she said. "He was always so easygoing."

Still there's one more dream Jhoy craves. "I want to dream about the night he was killed," she said. "I want to stab the person who stabbed him. So I can finally defend him."

A dream of vengeance may be the nearest thing to justice Jhoy and others can hope for. Few of the killers have been caught. ☐

victory in May 2016 by, among other things, promising to kill drug dealers and stop crime. According to police data, in Duterte's first six months at least 2,000 people were killed by police and another 4,000 by unknown assailants, perhaps vigilantes. Duterte vowed not to stop "until the last [drug] pusher on the streets is fully exterminated."

As the body count has risen, death rituals have become an increasingly common part of daily life in the Philippines. The rituals are

A woman checks her phone as she sits with her dog at dusk in Barangka Municipal Cemetery (above). People who live around the cemetery often hang out there. Before the dead are interred, mourners perform rituals to protect the living. A girl (below) is passed over the casket of Alex Hongco – it's believed this act will protect her from being haunted by the dead. Hongco, 31, was killed with five others; he left behind a wife and six children.

On the edge of five-year-old Francis Mañosca's coffin (above), mourners left food for chicks to peck at — a custom meant to prick the conscience of the killer. The boy and his father, Domingo Mañosca, were shot in their home. They left behind Francis's sisters, ages nine and one, and Domingo's wife, then nine months pregnant. A hearse (below) carries Hongco's coffin to the cemetery as some of his relatives walk behind.

CARVED

Centuries of eruptions have created hidden networks
of caves beneath Hawaii's volcanoes.

Last year's eruption of the Kilauea volcano, on Hawaii's Big Island, sent rivers of lava draining into the sea. Some of the molten rock gushed through tubes molded during previous episodes while other flows formed new tunnels, adding branches to the subterranean plumbing.

CJ KALE

BY LAVA

Author Joshua Foer explores Kazumura, the world's longest mapped lava tube, which stretches more than 40 miles and in places is the size of a subway tunnel. Its grooved walls took shape in the wake of an eruption approximately 600 years ago.

By Joshua Foer
Photographs by Carsten Peter

VETERAN CAVERS PETER AND ANN BOSTED WERE CRUISING AROUND THEIR HOMETOWN OF HAWAIIAN OCEAN VIEW, ON HAWAII'S BIG ISLAND, A FEW YEARS AGO WHEN ANN SPOTTED A SMALL HOLE OFF THE SIDE OF THE ROAD.

It was no more than three feet wide—just big and inviting enough for the couple to pull their car over and try to slink into.

"We had a couple hours to kill," Peter told me, "so we started surveying, and we found a side passage that turned out to be a lot more mazy than we expected." Back home, Peter marked the *puka,* or cave entrance, on a digital map and planned to return later—with the landowner's permission—to see where the opening might lead.

From outer space, the town of Hawaiian Ocean View looks like a thatched mat of asphalt draped over the side of Mauna Loa volcano. The 102-square-mile grid of crisscrossing streets and vacant lots is nearly twice the size of Washington, D.C., yet is home to fewer than 4,500 residents. You might think that only a pathological optimist would choose to build a house on the parched slope of an active volcano, but over the past two decades, Ocean View has become an international destination for cavers, who have come to explore and map the Kipuka Kanohina, a network of lava caves that course like veins 15 to 80 feet beneath the town.

There are two ways to make a cave: fast and slow. Many of the world's most iconic caves—Carlsbad Caverns and Lechuguilla in New Mexico, Mammoth Cave in Kentucky—were carved out over millions of years, by the plodding drip and flow of acidic water through soluble limestone.

By contrast, lava caves, widely known as lava tubes, are formed in a geological instant—a year or two, sometimes weeks—by an eruption from the Earth's crust.

Most of Hawaii's lava tubes are formed by a type of syrupy flow called *pahoehoe.* As it pours down the volcano, the lava at the surface is cooled by the air and solidifies, creating an elastic, skinlike outer layer. Beneath this inflating membrane, the lava continues to ooze, eroding the ground beneath it and carving underground tunnels. Now insulated from the air, the hot lava can surge unimpeded, often for many miles. As the eruption subsides and the channels drain their last molten contents, what's left behind is a massive, 3-D fun house of plumbing.

Probably no other place on Earth has as many accessible lava tubes as Hawaii, and probably no other town has proved such fertile terrain for their exploration as Ocean View.

IN THE 1990S, the Bosteds were active members of the team that mapped the 138-mile-long Lechuguilla Cave, widely regarded as one of the world's most beautiful. Now in their 60s and semiretired—Peter is a particle physicist affiliated with the College of William and Mary—they are among a handful of experienced cavers who have become full-time residents of Ocean View. Ann has pigtails down to her waist, and Peter sports a bright Hawaiian-print shirt, a white driver's cap, flip-flops, and a biblical-length white beard. They say they're now doing more caving than at any other point in their lives. They reckon that some years the two of them have spent more than 200 days underground.

Peter and Ann brought me back to explore the new roadside puka they'd discovered, along with another couple, Don and Barb Coons, Illinois grain farmers and lifelong cavers who winter in Ocean View. Don, 64, was a guide at Mammoth Cave for 10 years and spent 18 winters on the legendary expeditions that helped expand the map of Chevé in Oaxaca, Mexico, the second deepest cave in North America. He's the president of the Cave Conservancy of Hawaii, a nonprofit trust that has been buying up land in and around Ocean View to preserve the tunnels that lie beneath.

Wearing helmets, headlamps, and volleyball pads on our elbows and knees, we slither on our backs into the hole and army crawl for about a hundred yards through a previously mapped passage less than three feet tall. It has been centuries since lava flowed through this particular cave.

Festooned with trippy Dr. Seuss–like ornaments, the lava tubes of Hawaii seem to belong on another planet. Delicate lavacicles hang from the walls and ceilings like stalactites and take on a panoply of weird shapes, from spiky shark's teeth to bubbly, gooey driblet spires. Long, hollow soda straws, squeezed out of the ceiling by gas while the cave was cooling, hang in thick clusters. In spots, the cave's silvery, magnesioferrite glaze crinkles up like peeling paint. Elsewhere a thin layer of gypsum colors the walls a bright white, and mats of rock-eating bacteria excrete blue-green splotches of microbial poop.

Our army crawl ends at a junction where the ceiling dips down to less than a foot above the sharp, serrated floor. "This is our idea of fun," Peter says drily, as we wriggle forward on our bellies into the impossibly tight crawlway, my T-shirt audibly ripping on the jagged floor. The passage is too cramped for even our helmets to squeeze through, so we take them off and shimmy forward in the dark.

For all our scrapes, bruises, and torn clothing, our compensation this morning will be 154.4 feet of fresh cave added to the map of the Kipuka Kanohina network. That may not sound like much, but it's through days like this that the map inches toward completion at the rate of three to four miles a year. Kanohina may soon be the longest surveyed lava tube system in the world.

THE CAVE that the Kanohina system seems poised to supplant in the record books is on the other side of the Big Island. It was likely created during a 15th-century eruption of a different volcano, Kilauea. At more than 40 miles long, Kazumura is the longest lava tube mapped to date, and also the deepest. Though its roof is never more than a few dozen yards beneath the surface,

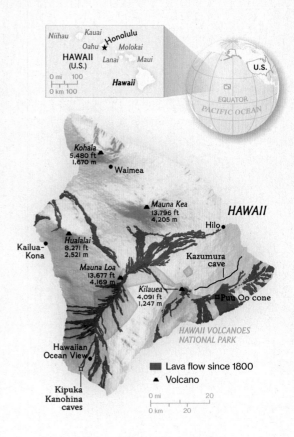

Of the Big Island's five volcanoes, only Kilauea, Mauna Loa, and Hualalai have erupted since 1800. Kilauea's Puu Oo eruption has been ongoing since 1983.

MATTHEW W. CHWASTYK, NGM STAFF
SOURCES: USGS, HAWAIIAN VOLCANO OBSERVATORY; NATIONAL PARK SERVICE

the vertical drop—from the top of the cave, midway up the volcano, down to its terminus near the coast—is 3,613 feet.

Unlike the Kanohina system, which consists of several parallel passages that interweave like the delta of a large river, Kazumura is mostly one long, gaping straight shot of a tunnel—so wide and tall (more than 60 feet) in parts that it feels as if it could be easily adapted for a subway train. Despite Kazumura's cavernous profile, the first through trip didn't take place until 1995, when it was completed in a two-day expedition.

"This is a national treasure, and yet there are people on this island who live right on top of the cave and don't even know it exists," says Harry Shick, a landowner who operates tours through a

A choose-your-own-adventure section of Kipuka
Kanohina splits into three tunnels, which will
narrow as cavers go deeper. Navigating lava rock
can be perilous. "The texture," says one caver, "is
like Velcro," capable of tearing clothing and cutting
skin. There are also dangers overhead: Chunks of
sharp lava can break off and fall from the ceiling.

HOW A LAVA TUBE IS FORMED

A VOLCANO ERUPTS

Molten rock and gas escape from deep beneath the Earth's surface, sending lava spewing out in effusive and sometimes explosive eruptions.

LAVA FLOWS

Factors like speed, gas content, and volume can yield two flow types: the rough and chunky *aa* or the smooth *pahoehoe*. Most lava tubes in Hawaii are formed by pahoehoe flows.

A COVERED CHANNELS As the slower moving sides of a lava channel gradually cool, solidify, and grow inward, the top of the flow can crust over, making a roof.

B INFLATED SHEETS On flatter slopes, pahoehoe flows can spread by inflating and pushing forward sheets of lava while maintaining a molten core.

LAVA IS INSULATED

As the outer layers of lava cool and solidify, they form an insulated tube, trapping heat and allowing the molten core to flow long distances.

A CAVE TAKES SHAPE

The volume of lava, speed of flow, and rate of erosion determine the nascent cave's depth, ceiling height, and shape.

Changing lava level

B INFLATED SHEETS

A COVERED CHANNELS

Floating chunks of hardened lava can gather into a logjam, which helps form a crust.

Tubes are often built atop previous lava flows, channels, and tubes — the new flow burying the old.

Flow ledge

Extreme heat can melt the solid lava at the tube's edges and base, enlarging the tube.

Original ground level

FORGED BY FIRE

Hawaii's basaltic shield volcanoes have produced some of the world's deepest and longest lava tubes — tunnels carved by rivers of molten rock. Caves etched by flowing water can take millions of years to form, while a volcanic eruption can generate miles of lava tubes in a matter of weeks or months. Thousands of these tubes twist, braid, and intersect beneath the surface of Hawaii's Big Island.

TUBES TO CAVES

After an eruption subsides, the remaining lava hardens, and some tubes can become accessible caves. Many have long served as an important part of native Hawaiian culture and as a source of water and shelter.

Secondary Formations

Flow ledges, stalactites, stalagmites, lava-level markings, and shiny or textured walls can occur from changes in lava levels and cooling rates.

Skylight

Stalactites

Lava-level marking

Flow ledge

Stalagmites

MANUEL CANALES, DAISY CHUNG, EVE CONANT, NGM STAFF; AMANDA HOBBS. ART: TOMÁŠ MÜLLER
SOURCES: DON COONS AND MICHAEL WARNER, CAVE CONSERVANCY OF HAWAII

LAVA ESCAPES

If the lava volume increases or debris blocks the tube, lava can push up through open "skylights" or burst through cracks, making new surface flows or tubes.

NEW LAND IS MADE

Since Kilauea's ongoing Puu Oo eruption began in 1983, hundreds of acres have been added to the south-east coast of Hawaii's Big Island.

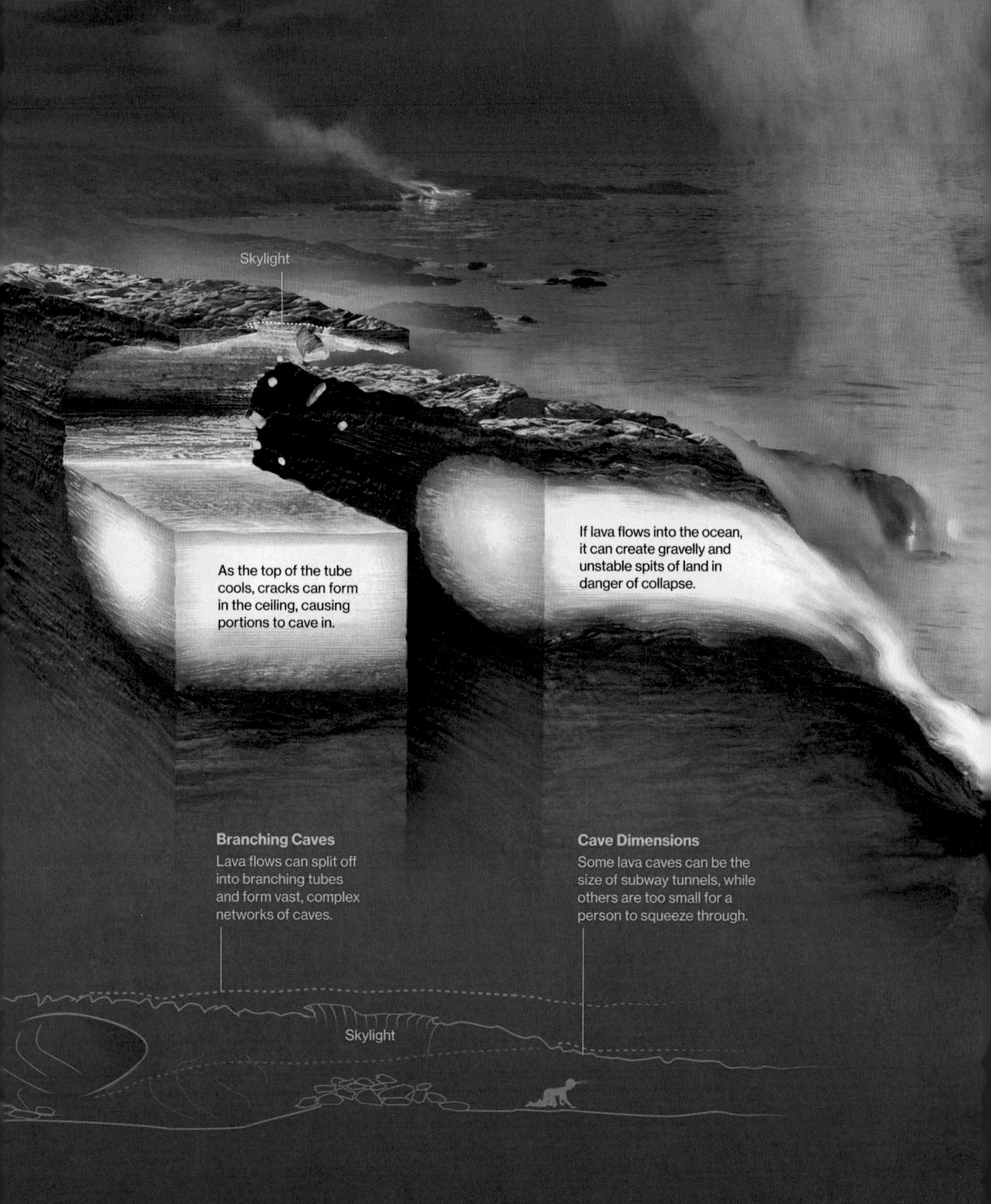

Skylight

As the top of the tube cools, cracks can form in the ceiling, causing portions to cave in.

If lava flows into the ocean, it can create gravelly and unstable spits of land in danger of collapse.

Branching Caves
Lava flows can split off into branching tubes and form vast, complex networks of caves.

Cave Dimensions
Some lava caves can be the size of subway tunnels, while others are too small for a person to squeeze through.

Skylight

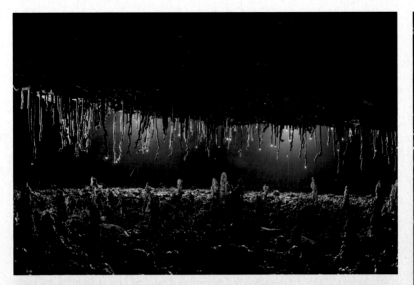

Lavacicles (top), a common feature, are squeezed out of a lava tube's roof by gases under high pressure and then cooled mid-drip. The gooey appearance of a rock wall (above) in Manu Nui cave was formed when the lava chemistry started to change and the iron contained in the lava oxidized into various minerals. Pristine freshwater pools (right) are rare in Hawaii's lava tubes. They may look inviting, but explorers say divers can become disoriented in the twisting passages or trapped by blockages or rockfall and run out of air.

stretch of Kazumura that lies under his property.

There is, it seems, an *omertà* that surrounds the Big Island's lava tubes. Most cavers and conservationists would prefer that outsiders never learn the locations of their finds. When the Bosteds offered to take me to a cave called Manu Nui that they've been mapping since 2003, it was on the condition that *National Geographic* not reveal its precise whereabouts, except to say that it was created by Hualalai, the island's third most historically active volcano, after Mauna Loa and Kilauea.

Manu Nui is, in many respects, the jewel of the island. With an average incline of 15.7 degrees, it

is one of the steepest lava tubes in Hawaii, and its features are surreal. After entering the cave through a mist-shrouded puka on private land, we head uphill to a chamber that could be a fantasy from Willy Wonka's Chocolate Factory. The walls, spattered in chocolate-, peanut butter-, cherry-, and butterscotch-colored drippings, look so luscious and fudgelike that I'm almost tempted to lick them. The Bosteds are keen to ensure the unique formations aren't disturbed by curious adventure seekers. A lavacicle is a fragile thing, and it takes only one misplaced handhold to permanently disfigure a cave. Shick has meticulously

gone through several miles of Kazumura, reattaching fallen features with superglue.

"We don't even fully understand these cave ecosystems," says Lyman Perry, from Hawaii's Division of Forestry and Wildlife, "so we don't want people going into them. The reality is that if people find out about these places, they're going to ruin them eventually."

Even more delicate than the caves' features are the cultural sensitivities that surround them. Many native Hawaiians consider lava tubes *kapu*, or sacred sites, because of their frequent use as ancient burial grounds. In Hawaiian tradition, bones contain a person's *mana,* or spiritual energy, and aren't to be unnecessarily disturbed.

Keoni Alvarez, a 31-year-old activist and filmmaker who has battled developers trying to build atop burial caves, says that whenever human remains are found inside a lava tube, they render the entire cave system, start to finish, kapu. "We believe our caves are sacred and should not be desecrated," he tells me. The problem is that no one can know whether a particular cave was used for ancient burials until it has been explored. Many native Hawaiians categorically refuse to venture into lava caves out of respect for what they might encounter inside.

But if modern Hawaiians tend to be wary of lava tubes, their ancestors clearly used them quite a bit. Many cave openings show evidence of prehistoric habitation, complete with hearths and sleeping terraces. In war, longer lava tubes were sealed and used as "refuge caves" to hide women, children, and elders. In some cases, stone walls were built across tube entrances, leaving a passage just big enough for a single person to climb through.

A local expert estimates that one in two caves on the Big Island contains some sort of archaeological artifact. Especially on the dry, leeward side of the island, freshwater is hard to come by, and lava tubes were often the best place to find it. Deep inside Kanohina, hundreds of yards from entrances, one frequently comes across remains of kukui-nut torches and rings of rocks that once propped up gourds used to collect dripping water.

DON COONS AND PETER BOSTED are insistent about the difference between adventure and exploration. Adventure is what you do when you're out for a thrill. Exploration is slow, methodical, and never for your sake alone. Every cave they explore, including this narrow, jagged section of the Kipuka Kanohina that we're crawling through, must be meticulously surveyed and mapped using clinometers and laser range finders.

"The deep sea, outer space, and caves: Those are the only frontiers left," says Coons, who does his exploring in a lightweight helmet with a small flashlight duct-taped to the brim. "On a working-man's salary, you can go into an unexplored place and discover something new and be the only person in history to see it."

Back in the roadside puka, our prone bodies pinched between the ceiling and floor, Bosted makes a disconcerting judgment call. "This seems a bit dangerous," he says in his dry monotone. "I have to exhale in order to get through." He announces that he's turning around, leaving the rest of us to figure out where the cave might lead.

Seven and a half body lengths farther on, we

reach a pile of breakdown rocks so heavy they can't be budged from our prostrate position. The lead ends here for now, but the cool breeze we feel flowing over our faces can mean only one thing: There is more cave to chase on the other side. □

Joshua Foer wrote about dolphin intelligence for the May 2015 issue. Carsten Peter's photographs of the Democratic Republic of the Congo's Nyiragongo volcano appeared in the April 2011 magazine.

Lava from Kilauea volcano pours out of tubes into the Pacific Ocean, its final destination. Much of this ever evolving landscape is a mystery: Researchers estimate that roughly 10 percent of Hawaii's lava tubes have been mapped.

DOUG PERRINE

The Side Effect

*For many people in Haiti, street vendors
are the main source of medicine.
For the vendors, it's a way to survive.*

BY ARNAUD ROBERT
PHOTOGRAPHS BY PAOLO WOODS AND GABRIELE GALIMBERTI

Claudine Jourdain, a 33-year-old from southern Haiti,
sells medicine on the busy streets of Port-au-Prince.

'You see, I put the ampicillin next to the Tylenol— a packet of pink pills, a packet of blue pills. The colors have to look good together. If my display doesn't catch the eye, no one will buy anything.'

Aristil Bonord adjusts the blue plastic bucket on his right shoulder as he speaks. Inside it, a steeple of multicolored pills in blister packs rises like a totem. A pair of scissors, used to divvy up the medicine, pokes out at the top. The whole thing is held together with rubber bands.

For more than 20 years Bonord has roamed the streets of Port-au-Prince with this tower of treatments, this chemical Babel. But he is not a pharmacist. He is a vendor.

In a little apartment in the Pacot neighborhood of the Haitian capital, merchants like Bonord are lined up to have their portraits taken by Paolo Woods and Gabriele Galimberti. The two photographers—working on a project about medical access in over two dozen countries—have long been fascinated by the city's wandering druggists.

Street dispensaries, they say, are the main source of medicine for many Haitians. "Pharmacists are an endangered species," explains Lionel Étienne, a local drug importer. "Medicine is considered an ordinary consumer good."

The portable pharmacies may look like contemporary art installations or candy store displays, but they can be as dangerous as Russian roulette. The government's lack of oversight allows untrained merchants like Bonord to obtain and sell pharmaceutical products: generic medicines from China, expired pills, counterfeit drugs imported from the Dominican Republic.

The activity is technically illegal, but the laws are rarely enforced by the Ministry of Public Health and Population. So the vendors sell anything they can get their hands on, from abortion pills to Viagra knockoffs. Sometimes they give bad advice to their clients. One seller told a teenager to take powerful antibiotics for his acne.

"Every time I see a street vendor, it is like a slap in the face," mutters the ministry's pharmacy director, Flaurine Joseph. "They are like time bombs, and we have almost no way to stop them."

To make these portraits, Woods and Galimberti used an 8 x 10 large-format view camera with film and a medium-format digital camera. A white wall served as the backdrop.

As the vendors waited to be photographed, they eyed their neighbors' goods, rarely speaking. It was their only respite from a long day in the brutal sun. They were glad for the break but worried that they were losing clients.

Woods and Galimberti say they want to make people aware that access to medicine, taken for granted in developed countries, is a challenge in many places. In Haiti vendors and customers alike have to make do with what they can.

"I chose this profession because times are hard here," says Bonord. "I want my children to go to school. And everyone needs medicine." □

Vendors act as pharmacists and confessors. "People have no secrets from us," says Rénold Germain, 26. "They tell us about their infections, digestion, and sexual matters. For each problem we have a pill."

Julène Clerger, 37, and her husband, Pélège Aristil (right), 35, have five children at home. She's thinking about quitting the pharmaceutical business and selling bananas and boiled eggs instead. Aristil may eventually leave the trade as well. Later this year, when he finishes his theological studies, he'll be an accredited evangelical pastor.

Ady Dumé (left), 38, and
Aristil Bonord, 36, sell their
pharmaceutical products
on the street. Some vendors
have stands or kiosks in
local markets. Others pack
their pills into suitcases
and ride the public buses
of Port-au-Prince, in search
of additional sales.

STING OPERATION

By Catherine Zuckerman

Beehives six feet wide cling to cliffs in the jungles of eastern Nepal. To and from these structures fly enormous Himalayan bees—the makers of a hallucinogenic honey so powerful that its psychotropic effects can last up to 24 hours.

Harvesting this honey would seem to be an impossible endeavor. The job requires poking at angry, swarming bees while dangling 300 feet in the air on a ladder handwoven of bamboo strips. Still, for a man named Mauli Dhan (right), the modest profit he receives for collecting "mad honey" outweighs the risk of being stung hundreds of times and possibly falling to his death.

Perhaps Dhan remains safe because he had the dream. In the Kulung tribe, to which he belongs, tradition holds that only those who've had a specific dream can lead a honey hunt. Dhan had it at age 15. Now, after jeopardizing his life for more than four decades, he would like to retire. The question is: Has anyone else in his tribe had the dream?

To go FURTHER into the perilous job of honey hunting, watch a 360-degree video at *natgeo.com/honeyhunters360,* and read Mark Synnott's feature story in the July issue of *National Geographic.*

PHOTO: RENAN OZTURK